# GREEN DESIGN

A Guide to the
Environmental Impact of
Building Materials

Avril Fox
Robin Murrell

Architecture Design and Technology Press
London

Architecture Design and Technology Press
128 Long Acre
London
WC2E 9AN

First published 1989

British Library Cataloguing in Publication Data
A CIP catalogue record for this book is available from the British Library.

ISBN 1 85454 200 1

Publisher's Note
This book is not printed on recycled paper, despite every effort to find a
suitable, affordable paper. At the time of going to press (September 1989)
the UK recycled paper industry is not producing sufficient paper of high
enough quality and durability for general book publishing. This situation is
changing rapidly and we are sure that in the future a higher proportion of
books will be printed on recycled paper as a matter of course.

Printed in Great Britain by Bath Press.

# Contents

# Acknowledgements

Sources during research were too numerous to mention: to some we are indeed grateful, others were slippery and one or two were downright rude. We found rather sadly that inside the building industry there were individuals and even firms who cared quite deeply about environmental effects but had been forced to be cautious about letting this be known. We hope this situation changes soon.

Shiningly helpful were the staff of the Department of Energy: in our opinion they should all have their salaries doubled, while the Department's resources, recently cut, should not only be restored but increased. Special thanks, too, to Darrell Burns of Armitage Shanks in Rugeley for so patiently explaining the complexities of British loos.

Avril Fox
Robin Murrell

Dedicated to the memory of Marguerite Caroline Fox, who taught us to think about these things.

# Introduction

Architects and designers are beginning to be conscious that the materials they specify and the construction techniques they recommend all have an impact on the environment. There is increasing pressure from clients, both public and private, for environmental considerations to become a factor in design and in choosing materials. But the busy professional has no time individually to research the origins and composition of each of the many materials in use in the building process and at present there is no comprehensive source of information on the subject.

*Green Design* is intended to fill this gap, providing information on materials and processes in a form which will also be comprehensible to clients. It must be pointed out that the scene is continuously changing as ecological knowledge grows, so that extensions to our awareness will undoubtedly have occurred by the time this book is being read, but we have endeavoured to be as up-to-date as possible. The information is presented in alphabetical order, with an appendix, so as to simplify rapid access, as well as to offer background information which may be useful when choices have to be made. We believe that the facts we provide will enable designers and consumers to look in a new and innovative way at the materials they use.

The first consideration to arise when starting research was: how does one assess the environmental desirability of a product? Apart from considerations of the energy consumed in its extraction and processing, there is the question of the human cost, such as the extraction of materials from the earth at great physical hazard. The amount of energy expended in transport to the site of consumption is also a major consideration, and environmentally-conscious designers endeavour to cut down the distances over which materials have to be delivered. Moreover, good builders, designers and consumers are beginning to recognise that it is better to search the locality for attractive materials than to order things that have to be sent over long distances, and that buildings reflecting local influences and crafts have a special attraction. Another general principle when endeavouring to achieve harmony with ecological laws is to use materials which are as natural as possible, and have not changed much in being processed. In dealing with wood, for example, it is better to use permethrin, turpentine, pitch, beeswax and natural oils and stains, and in domestic use to avoid aerosols and choose wax polishes, lemon juice, and various vinegars.

A difficulty which arises in compiling such a work of reference is the close relationship between some headings. Readers interested, for example, in Energy would do well to consult also Waste and Fuel, and we have indicated many such relationships in order to render consultation easier.

We began by asking the following general questions:

**What is the raw material source?**
A fundamental ecological principle is the use of renewable raw materials. Wood, if it comes from a sustainable source, is renewable, whereas metal, plastic, gravel, sand and stone-based materials such as cement, concrete and plaster, once used, have gone for good; their use is consumption of the Earth itself. This is a relatively new concept; up to now the building industry has assumed that supplies are infinite. Yet we all know of instances of materials which were once regarded as commonplace but are now no longer obtainable. Tropical hardwoods provide past and present examples of this situation. The availability of mahogany from the islands of the West Indies was taken completely for granted by Victorian builders and, as a result, the types then used were more or less wiped out by over-exploitation. At the present moment the building industry is using up the last stocks of ramin, and certain types of South American mahogany will disappear within the next

few years. A widely used substitute, iroko, is now being used as if it is plentiful, but in fact it has all but disappeared from some countries which hitherto supplied it, and as no attempts appear to be made elsewhere in West Africa to sustainably-manage remaining forests it will no doubt be on the edge of extinction within the foreseeable future.

**Is the process of obtaining the raw material environmentally destructive?**

The extraction of certain materials is totally destructive of water tables and wildlife habitats. Major examples are limestone, sand, gravel, asbestos and open-cast mining for coal. Environmental pressures are already being exerted where such extraction is encroaching on sensitive sites. It is therefore increasingly urgent for substitutes to be devised or methods changed in order that our dependence on limestone and aggregates disappears as soon as possible.

**What is the true cost?**

Energy can be consumed in manufacturing, transporting, installing and maintaining material. Savings in energy resulting from the use of the material or design technique concerned must be a factor in assessing that material or technique, as there may be instances in which using an energy-expensive material may be justified by savings elsewhere in the structure or by substantially lower running or maintenance costs. But there are certain materials which in their production consume and waste colossal amounts of energy. These are the 'high-temperature process industries': iron and steel; iron casting; aluminium; copper; glass; potteries and ceramics; bricks; heavy engineering; cement and chemicals. Vast amounts of this energy is thrown away in waste gas streams, and pressure is now being put on the Government to legislate for conservation of this energy by heat-recovery methods. In the meantime consumers must become aware that every time they use the products of these industries they are contributing to the wastage of energy on a colossal scale.

There is another aspect to the energy debate which should

become a major issue: the use of labour. A fundamental Green principle is that labour is a renewable source of energy. It follows that its substitution, especially in the form of craftsmanship, for high-energy expenditure on materials and manufacturing processes, is environmentally desirable. Another principle is that energy should be expended as closely as possible to its need. The original village or noble estate supplied its own blacksmith, farrier, dressmaker, hairdresser, carpenter and joiner, shoemaker, leech, herbalist, builder and so on, and a great deal of its own food. A return to this self-contained village pattern would contribute tremendously to lowering energy expenditure on costly transport, lessening the present congestion of our roads. It would also tend towards full employment. Interestingly, technological advance in communications will assist this change of pattern; the advent of the energy-efficient micro-chip facilitates local self-sufficiency, rendering obsolete the need constantly to travel back and forth, and making it possible to identify the nearest source of materials and labour.

Even economists are beginning to realise that hidden environmental costs should be included when assessing expenditure. We have to learn how to price eco-values before making final decisions.

**How efficient in time is the product?**
The potential lifespan of a structure once completed is a matter of environmental concern. Any artefact which is constructed to last is more environment-friendly than an object with a limited shelf-life; a concept based purely on the profit motive. The Tudor, Georgian and Victorian buildings still in existence, which were sturdily built, are also – once damp-proofed – more comfortable to live and work in than present-day edifices deliberately built to be temporary. 'Designed obsolescence' is a notion completely opposed to the Green ethic, whether it is applied to a small piece of kitchen equipment or an office block. We must seek to return to a situation in which everything that is produced is designed eventually to become as desirable an antique, say, as an old bentwood rocking-chair.

**Can it be recycled?**
Structures which cannot by their nature last indefinitely, such as clothing, should be made from materials which can be recycled when they are discarded. The same principle applies to furniture, furnishings and the materials used in service supplies. Therefore when high-energy materials, such as metals, are used they should be employed in ways which facilitate recovery in due course. At the time of writing the design, for example, of most current plumbing and electrical systems render the recycling of the materials all but impossible.

Potential disadvantages under one of these headings may be offset by benefits under another. For example, bricks are a 'high-energy use' product during manufacture and transport, and obtaining the raw material is an environmentally disruptive process. However, it can be argued that because they are extremely durable if employed correctly, and in theory easy to recycle when the structure concerned is demolished, on balance they are a relatively benign alternative to manufactured composite materials. But not as benign as the use of renewable wood, used as in Scandinavian structures.

*Green Design* is also written for special-interest groups who seek more information on what things are made from, and this often provides the intelligent consumer with dilemmas. Vegetarians and those who fight for animal rights will be interested to know that rooms in which formaldehyde adhesives are used, in chipboard and Melamine cabinet interiors and worktops, contain animal products, because formaldehyde (a constituent of Melamine) is derived from bones, hides and other slaughterhouse waste. On the other hand, there are those who regard the by-products of animal husbandry as a renewable resource and are more concerned about the destruction of forests. The Green movement is not monolithic: like all new ethical systems it simply brings before us fresh areas of responsible choice.

In trying to apply Green principles we have discovered that in many cases insufficient information exists at present to enable us to make exact comparisons. Also the durability and efficiency of many materials depends on whether they are correctly employed in the structure concerned, and whether or not construction work has been carried out properly. Materials which might seem obvious candidates for efficient recycling may be employed in ways which makes it impossible to save them during demolition. This is obviously something to be borne in mind by architects and builders during the construction of buildings. Building-maintenance costs and the natural resistance of certain materials to pollution damage also need to be considered. Some materials and techniques used when cleaning and restoring the exterior of buildings are themselves environmentally questionable.

It has therefore proved best to use expressions such as 'low energy use', 'inherently durable' and 'limited potential for recycling' rather than attempt detailed comparative evaluations. It is to be hoped that even such generalised comparisons will stimulate debate on these aspects of materials and encourage manufacturers to be more forthcoming with information in the future.

However, some materials and practices in current use in the building industry are of such concern that they should be blacklisted for all who take a responsible attitude to the environment. They are:

### 1 The use of non-renewable tropical hardwoods

The building industry is a massive and almost indiscriminate user of tropical hardwoods and boards manufactured from tropical timber. Not only are most of the timber species involved directly endangered by irresponsible timber extraction, but in the countries concerned irreversible climatic and other changes are taking place as a result of the felling of the forests. The clearing of tropical rainforests has been shown to be a significant factor in the 'greenhouse effect', both directly by releasing $CO_2$ to the environment and indirectly by regional changes in rainfall patterns. Moreover, most of the landslides and mudslides which have destroyed mountain villages and killed thousands of people are directly attributable to deforestation. So far, the industry has shown only modest interest in switching to alternative timber sources and materials.

However, the use of tropical hardwoods which are from sustainably-managed forests should be encouraged, especially if it involves switching much of the timber conversion work to the country of origin. In one project (see Appendix), the timber bought from Java via the Indonesian Government supply organisation is not only contractually guaranteed to be from sustainably-managed forests (in this instance first planted by the Dutch at the turn of the century) but the timber is shipped sawn to required sizes in Java. As their costs of timber conditioning and log conversion are lower than those in this country, this has not only resulted in increasing cash flow to Indonesia but has also produced substantial end-user cost savings due to reductions in manufacturing waste factors.

## 2 CFCs in building
These gases, which are a major cause of the depletion of the ozone layer, are still widely used in the manufacture of foams for building industry use. Alternatives now exist and there is no excuse for continued employment of CFCs.

## 3 Poor thermal-insulation standards
It is still general practice within the building industry to create structures which meet the minimum thermal insulation standards required by the building regulations. If all houses and commercial buildings were properly insulated for energy conservation we would not only save millions in heating costs but would also cut down on the number of new power stations we need. New government legislation is needed to promote maximum energy conservation in buildings.

The Government is about to tackle the question of energy-saving and this may give rise to much tougher standards in the near future (in construction terms). The whole subject of energy management and the creation of structures which use energy dynamically needs to be considered – for example, combined heat and power from waste, which even in an office context is beginning to become worth considering. Also, small-scale fluidised-bed plants which sell spare power to the grid are coming in. Finally, the point needs to be made that energy-saving is cheaper if it is a fundamental feature of the building, rather than either something added as an afterthought or the subject of changes after the building has been around for some time.

### 4  Toxic chemicals

Certain extremely dangerous pesticides which are banned in all other situations are still in common use for timber treatment purposes in the building industry. The manufacture, use and disposal of substances used in timber treatment are at present common causes of the release of heavy metals and toxic organic substances into the environment through uncontrolled dumping and poor site control. There are also cases of human sickness and even death which seem to have arisen from the use of these substances. Here again government legislation is urgently needed.

### 5  Paints and solvents

Not only does the manufacture of these frequently result in the gross pollution of British rivers, but incorrect employment on site and uncontrolled disposal of residues give rise to pollution in usage by heavy metals and organochlorines. In general, the manufacture of paints, solvents, paper pulp, aluminium and certain other materials in widespread use in building involve the creation of more or less toxic wastes, at present mainly dumped in landfill sites or released into rivers, sewers or the atmosphere, whence they are all eventually recycled to human settlements, the sea or the wild, and are then practically indestructible. Nature cannot deal with chemicals which were not produced by Nature.

The following can, as a result of current or proposed EC Directives, be expected to be the subject of further controls shortly: Mercury; Cadmium; Polychlorinated biphenyls (PCBs); Polychlorinated triphenyls (PCTs); Carbon tetrachloride (TCT); Organotin compounds; Lindane/hexachlorocyclohexane (HCH); Titanium dioxide manufacturing wastes; Oil from refineries and reception facilities.

It is interesting that a large number of environmentally-objectionable materials used in the building industry have in the last two or three years been withdrawn from production or modified in ways which, quite incidentally, make them more environment-friendly because of the need to meet more stringent Health and Safety regulations and standards during their manufacture. For instance, detergent cleaning materials, especially enzyme-type cleaners, offered by the major manufacturers have been modified quite substantially in order to reduce health risks for those employed in their manufacture. These regulations are under continuous review and the benefits to the environment which flow from this will be quite considerable.

A common attitude which emerged during research was succinctly expressed by a representative of the Council for the Protection of Rural England: 'Need for a material is apparently determined by an ability to sell it rather than by a balance between the desirability of the end product and the consequences of extracting the raw material'. Our eventual and regretful conclusion was that we have a long way to go before extractors and manufacturers automatically consider the ecological cost of a product as automatically as they assess its possible market. We hope this book will help to change this unacceptable situation.

# A

## ACID RAIN

There is no detailed theory of how rainwater becomes acid, but the general mechanism is that it is caused by the incorporation of trace substances in the atmosphere, later to be precipitated as rain. Sulphur compounds in particular, formed by burning coal and oil, produce sulphurous acid when dissolved in rain.

Stone facades are the most vulnerable; during the wetting process the acid in the rain reacts with carbonates in limestones, dolomites, calcareous sandstones and mortars. This acid solution penetrates the stone to a degree dependent upon its porosity and chemical nature, and when the water evaporates the acid particles remain as deposits. On limestone buildings in particular, rainwater acidified by carbon dioxide and sulphur dioxide slowly dissolves away the stone. The surface then acts as host to algal growths, and green stains and slime appear. Acid rain also causes lead on the exterior of buildings to become thin and finally erode away completely through the continuous effect of the rainwater.

## ACRYLICS

(See Plastics)

## ADHESIVES

Generally colloidal solutions which set to a hard film adhering to the surface of other materials. Animal glues are forms of collagen (a protein) and may be produced from slaughterhouse wastes such as bone, hide and horn, from fish bones, or from soured milk curds (casein). They are water-soluble and usually contain preservatives. Vegetable glues (known as mucilages) such as starches, gums, gum arabic and tragacanth are also water-soluble.

Waterglass, cellulose and its derivatives, pitch and latex rubber are natural adhesives. All of the above are renewable products, unless we cease to domesticate and eat animals, and thus in themselves environmentally acceptable in use.

Synthetic adhesives are mainly thermoplastic or thermosetting, and non-renewable. In the first category, polymers such as polystyrene, asphalt and polyvinyl compounds remain soluble after setting and melt when heated. They have the advantage of being flexible in use. Most thermosetting adhesives, such as epoxy resins and polyesters, are insoluble and chemically inert once set. They are set by either heat or use of a catalyst and tend to be rigid or semi-rigid after setting (see Solvents).

Apart from considerations of renewability, environmental concern about adhesives relates mainly to the solvents with which some are associated in use. For example, gas given off by chipboard bonded with formaldehyde-based glues has given rise to special design and constructional precautions in furniture applications in some countries.

The durability of many items in which adhesives are involved is often governed more by the characteristics of the adhesive than those of the basic materials concerned. For example, PVA and casein glues used as timber adhesives may have an indefinite predicted life in dry conditions which can be reduced to five years or substantially less in the presence of moisture.

AGGREGATES

The term covers sand, gravel, broken stone and brick fragments. These are known as 'metals' in some parts of the trade, and are covered by the Town and Country Planning (Minerals) Act, 1981. Guidelines concerning their extraction were issued by the Department of the Environment in 1982, and revised guidelines are expected shortly. Until recently extraction of sand and gravel has been possible in less-sensitive areas but such areas have now mostly been exhausted, and in many parts of Britain struggles are going on to prevent extraction from various sensitive sites. Extraction is environmentally destructive. The use of aggregates can sometimes be avoided by rehabilitating existing buildings, and approaches to buildings, rather than erecting new dwellings.

If new building is essential, steel-framed or timber-framed construction is preferable, now that moisture problems in the latter type of building have been overcome. It is unfortunate that in the UK current planning regulations mitigate against the erection of wood-walled dwellings which, when the wood is from a sustainable source, are effective, warm and environmentally beneficial. Pressure for amendment of planning regulations to encourage the erection of timber-walled dwellings would help to mitigate the aggregate problem.

An alternative to sand and gravel is crushed rock, of which there are vast resources, and which is extracted with less environmental damage (see Stone). In 1987 the total extraction of aggregates in the UK was 143 million tonnes of hard rock, over 111 million tonnes of sand and gravel, 16 million tonnes of which was sea-dredged, a process which destroys the marine environment. Most gravel is used for making concrete, but it is also used loose in various surfacing projects, and, coated with a bituminous material, in asphalt. Sand goes mainly into mortar for brickwork, exterior renderings, and to a lesser extent into glass-making (see Glass) and foundry work.

While it is true that after extraction of sand and gravel, which takes many years, the land can be rehabilitated, existing colonies of badgers, stoats, field-mice, butterflies and so on cannot be replaced, and natural springs are destroyed. Also, rehabilitation is often unsatisfactory; subsoil, for example, is sometimes put back over topsoil, rendering the surface infertile.

'Secondary Aggregates' is the term used for rubble from demolition, which is either tipped or used for a variety of purposes, including infilling, sub-bases and low-grade concrete.

The question of potential recycling of aggregates needs to be explored further, in view of the virtual impossibility of obtaining fresh supplies in ways which are environmentally benign. Various manufactured building blocks are already made from recycled waste materials but there is considerable potential for the recycling of reprocessed demolition waste in secondary contexts as both hard core and aggregates.

AIR-CONDITIONING

A complex process in which atmospheric air is cleaned and brought to a desired temperature and humidity prior to entering a building.

The designers of air-conditioning systems try to minimise the amount of air that has to be taken from outside, but if they take in too little there can be problems; the unpleasant organisms which are already in the building can multiply. There are many health hazards in totally-sealed air-conditioned buildings: Legionnaire's Disease; the spread of colds; and the effects of dry air exacerbation (sore throats, bronchitis and discomfort with contact lenses, etc.). Humidifying the air brings its own difficulties, such as an increased likelihood of Legionnaire's Disease, which breeds in humidifier plants. Static electricity, too, is increased by dry air, giving rise to electric shocks. Absenteeism caused by colds, etc., has been found to be 20 per cent higher among staff in air-conditioned offices. It has also to be remembered that air-conditioners which contain chlorofluorocarbons (CFCs) in their mechanisms are contributing to the release of these into the atmosphere, and damaging the ozone layer. However, systems are coming into use which do not use CFCs, and some local authorities are already putting into operation methods for recycling CFCs in existing equipment when discarded.

The other consideration about air-conditioning plants is that they are the principal source of infection by Legionnaire's Disease, due to droplet infection from a plant which has not be properly maintained. New systems which do not involve the release of potentially infected water vapour to the atmosphere are now gradually being adopted.

Bearing these considerations in mind, it seems unnecessary to design for temperate climates any building incorporating air-conditioning, apart from special situations such as hospital operating-theatres. We can control the energy output and energy losses of the building by the overall form, the construction of the external walls, insulation, window size and type, shading and so on.

Such energy-efficient buildings also have the advantage that those within can exercise some control over the ambient atmosphere; one of the major criticisms of air-conditioned, sealed buildings by those working in them is the inability to exercise this control.

When there is a specific need artificially to regulate the atmosphere, and an appropriate air-conditioning system, preferably dry-cooled, is properly selected and rigorously maintained, it can be advantageous, but such special needs are rarer than is commonly assumed.

Before air-conditioning was invented, the great Arab architects used window design, shading ledges, central domes creating cool draughts, careful orientation, and insulating walls to create cool buildings, and succeeded even in the hottest climates. The principles of these ingenious, age-old constructions have been explained by the Egyptian architect Hassan Fathy.

*Building Use Studies* recently completed an investigation of staff reports of building-related symptoms of malaise now medically recognised as the Sick Buildings Syndrome (see Appendix). They questioned 4300 workers in 47 buildings. Overall 34 per cent described the air in their offices as uncomfortably dry, hot or stuffy; over half reported physical symptoms such as lethargy, headache or irritation of eyes, nose and throat when at work; and 25 per cent felt that working conditions reduced their productivity by over 20 per cent. These complaints were higher in air-conditioned buildings, which are usually also sealed buildings, so that the individual's ability to modify temperature and ventilation, or control their access to the sound and sense of the outside, is eliminated. Open-plan offices were found to have higher rates of sickness than conventional offices (see also Ducted Air).

ALCOHOL                (See Fuel; Energy; Solvents)

ALUMINIUM              The manufacture of aluminium involves high energy use, though this can be offset to some extent by utilising its special characteristics to reduce the amount of metal used or to extend the durability of structures or items in which it is incorporated. The heat involved in manufacture could also be conserved. So long as the design or construction approach does not make it impossible to recover the material in a reasonably unadulterated form, the potential for recycling aluminium is considerable (see also Metals).

ASBESTOS

Silicate mineral occurring as a glassy rock which can be split into thin fibres, enabling it to be shaped into ropes, fireproof material, plasterboard, etc. Its advantages are that in building products it is strong in tension, flexible, and with resistance to flames, alkalis, acids, neutral salts and organic solvents. The major disadvantage is that asbestos dust, breathed in, can settle in the lungs and solidify, giving rise to the disease asbestosis, which is eventually fatal, and the incurable cancer mesothelioma. Therefore the use of materials incorporating asbestos in a form in which such dust can be released must be avoided. Asbestos can safely be used when any tendency to release fibres into the air is removed, such as by encapsulation by a flexible membrane or by retention in a cement matrix. Such safe usage is exemplified in asbestos silica-lime products, vinyl-asbestos floor tiles and bitumen felts utilised in insulation, roofing, flue pipes and wallboards. Asbestos cement is also widely used, but regular checks must be made to see that in weathering and wear and tear no dust has been released. Asbestos is also used in spray coatings, but these must be sealed and kept sealed for safety.

The mining of asbestos involves moving enormous amounts of rock in order to extract the approximately 5 per cent fibrous material. Usually it is an open-cast operation, but deep mining does occur, and in this case powerful, energy-consuming ventilating systems are necessary to renew the air and filter out the dust.

Many minerals other than asbestos exhibit fibrous structures and are then known as 'asbestiform'. All mining operations, therefore, whether for quarries, tunnels or roads can give rise to inhalation of dangerous fibrous dusts if the proper precautions are not taken.

Open-cast asbestos mining is attracting interest as a source of, for example, aggregates for asphalt (see Bitumen), metals, magnesium compounds and mineral wool. In Canada some of these sources are already being exploited.

Open-cast mining of course completely destroys the environment, habitats and water tables. Most Canadian companies re-vegetate and rehabilitate the area when extraction is finished, but this is not a universal practice, and in other countries environmental rehabilitation is patchy.

Only the largest deposits of asbestos are commercially exploited, and these are in Brazil, Canada, China, Colombia, Cyprus, Greece, India, Italy, Japan, Korea, South Africa, the USSR, Taiwan, Turkey, the USA, Yugoslavia and Zimbabwe.

Asbestos waste must be placed in sealed labelled containers or, if it is mixed with other waste, should not consist of more than 5 per cent of the whole.

ASPHALT

A viscous or solid hydrocarbon compound obtained from the distillation of heavy crude oils or alternatively from naturally-occuring surface deposits. These deposits of 'lake asphalt' arise when crude oil reaches the surface and the lighter fractions evaporate.

The energy expended in obtaining lake asphalt is small, and distilled asphalt is an otherwise wasted by-product of the oil-refining process. The durability of asphalt in use is very dependent on design and installation. The potential exists for recycling in most contexts and worn macadam road surfaces are often reprocessed. Therefore, as so often, the environmental desirability of the material depends entirely upon the manner in which the material is exploited (see Bitumen).

ASTERITE

A suspension of aluminium oxide in an acrylic base used to form a sheet material which can be processed using hand tools or machines suitable for joinery work. The material is also thermoplastic and can be moulded to form quite complex shapes. Sheets can be joined using a proprietory resin glue to form continuous surfaces (see Plastics).

**BATS**

(See Pesticides; Preservatives)

**BIOFUEL (BIOMASS)**

Any solid, liquid or gaseous fuels produced from organic materials, either directly from plants or indirectly from industrial, commercial or agricultural wastes. The great environmental benefit of biomass use is its permanent renewability. At 1988 energy costs, wastes recycled as biofuels in the UK could contribute more than four million tonnes a year of coal equivalent. Given modest increases in energy prices, the size of the contribution could rise to fifteen million tonnes by 2025. This applies to both dry and wet wastes such as sewage, animal wastes and industrial effluents. Wastes with an energy content of twenty-one million tonnes of coal equivalent are discarded in the UK every year. In Brazil, sugar-canes, pines and eucalypts are crops used for biofuel. However, to burn biofuels effectively without harm to the environment special equipment has to be created. The design of systems for this purpose with capital and operating costs which compete with plant which burns fossil fuels offers an exciting challenge to engineers.

Straw is already used as a biofuel in buildings adjacent to farms, such as Woburn Abbey. Other examples are the biogas digester at South Caernarvon Creameries; the Byker Reclamation Plant at Newcastle upon Tyne, and the Commonwork Land Trust at Chiddingston, Kent, which produces methane gas from a digester of cattle manure and uses it to dry hand-made bricks from clay out of its own land. At University College, Cardiff, a cyclone combustor with integral ash removal is showing promise. This project is funded by the Department of Energy together with Coal Processing Consultants Ltd. In Eire there are examples of straw obtained from adjacent farmland being used by hotels not only for complete central heating but also to warm swimming pools with the extra heat available. Sawdust is another valuable potential source for exploitation under this heading (see also Fuel).

BITUMEN

A tarry residue consisting almost entirely of a mixture of carbon and large hydrocarbon molecules which is a by-product of the distillation of crude oil, lignite or coal. It also occurs occasionally in asphalt lakes.

Bitumen comprises various mixtures of hydrocarbons, usually taken to mean the solid or tarry mixture obtained as a residue when coal tar or petroleum are distilled. It is widely used in building trade applications which call for a waterproof and thermoplastic material with adhesive characteristics. It is therefore usually combined with other materials, such as aggregates, woven textiles or paper (see Asphalt).

Bitumen is an inherently low-energy material of considerable durability if correctly employed and installed. When used for roofing or road or walkway surfaces it can often be recycled extensively as part of the maintenance process. From the environmental point of view, therefore, it is largely benign so long as we continue to exploit crude oil and various types of coal.

BLINDS

These can be of fundamental importance in ecologically-conscious design. In temperate climates the complications and expense of air-conditioning can be avoided – except in special cases such as hospital operating-theatres – by the skilled use of openable windows and appropriate blinds. In semi-tropical areas the same applies. In the hottest climates, before the advent of air-conditioning, elegant and highly-skilled devices exploiting blinds were invented for cooling the air (see Air-conditioning).

BLOCKS

The usual definition of blocks used in the building industry is that they need to be lifted with two hands; bricks can be lifted with one, and two people are needed to lift a slab. However, there are also differences in materials used and methods of employment. Generally speaking, blocks are used in hidden situations and then surfaced with other materials. It is therefore upon cost, weight, ease of installation and the simplicity with which they can be integrated with other elements of the design and installation process that the choice of blocks depends. Clay blocks are generally extruded hollow units and are often surfaced to simplify finishing with plaster or other coatings. Precast concrete blocks and masonry units vary from heavy and dense blocks to lightweight blocks incorporating aerated mortars or lightweight aggregates. The environmental attitude towards the use of blocks is neutral at the moment, balancing energy-expenditure in manufacture against the energy-saving function of insulation by blocks. If manufacturers conserved waste energy, all blocks were made from waste materials, and no raw materials were obtained destructively, blocks would become environmentally-desirable.

| Type | Energy employed | Durability in use | Recycling potential |
|------|-----------------|-------------------|---------------------|
| Clay | High energy | Indefinite | Moderate |
| Cement | | | |
| dense | High energy | Indefinite | Limited |
| lightweight | Medium energy Indefinite | Limited | |

Lightweight blocks usually possess good thermal insulation properties, contributing to energy-saving. Many proprietory lightweight blocks now utilise industrial waste materials, such as fly ash, in their composition. But all clay products involve open-pit quarrying, which is of course totally destructive of habitats and water-tables.

BOARDS

Many types of preformed boards and sheets are now in common use in the building industry. They vary considerably in their environmental impact, which depends partly on their composition and partly on their potential for eco-friendly use in less-destructive construction methods.

In seeking alternatives to systems which involve the extensive use of cement and concrete or other limestone-based building materials, many types of boards can be used to extend the possibilities of timber-frame, all-wood and other desirable alternative methods of construction. The environmental disadvantage of building boards is that they offer very little potential for recycling. However, so long as suitable clauses are used in specifications to exclude the use of environmentally-objectionable materials such as tropical hardwoods and certain adhesives, this negative factor is balanced by their efficient use of other materials from renewable sources. Scrap boards, also, can be incinerated with other non-recyclable waste to produce energy.

Considering the available boards from an environmental point of view, the following characteristics emerge:

### Plywood
The durability of plywood is potentially considerable, depending on the suitability of its application. Unfortunately, this excellent method of creating high-performance building boards for a wide variety of purposes from timbers which might not be of commercial value otherwise has made a substantial contribution to the destruction of tropical rain-forests. The only reason for the use of tropical timber in this context is that it is cheaper than that from sustainable sources, but in environmental terms tropical hardwoods used for plywood are hideously expensive. The solution is to demand plywoods composed of softwoods or temperate hardwoods, unless a contractual guarantee is available from the supplier that the woods employed are the product of sustainably managed forests. Even then it is worth checking with Friends of the Earth that the infrastructure actually does exist in the country concerned to implement such a policy.

Pressure should be put on Western governments to implement a licensing scheme whereby it would be impossible to import tropical timber unless it bore a guarantee that it was obtained from properly-managed forests.

### Densified Laminated Wood
A group of specialised products of similar basic character to plywood but with special uses. The same comments generally apply.

### Blockboard and Laminboard
Boards of composite construction formed from cores of solid wood strips and covered with one or more layers of wood veneer. Certain specialised blockboards incorporate layers of other materials, such as vapour barriers. These composite boards are potentially high-performance materials made very efficiently from timbers from temperate sources. Tropical hardwoods are very rarely employed in their manufacture and can be excluded by a specification clause as suggested above.

### Fibre Insulating Board
The materials used in proprietary and unbranded insulating boards may be from a variety of sources. Absence of material from tropical forest sources cannot be guaranteed in most cases, but a specification clause precluding such material should be considered. Bearing this precaution in mind, most fibreboards are inherently Green in character and have an essential role to play in low-energy alternative construction systems.

### Plasterboard
The gypsum contained in such boards is hydrated calcium sulphate obtained from certain clays, shales or limestones. As such it is an energy-hungry material derived from non-renewable sources and alternative fillers for wallboards should therefore be devised.

### Particle Board (Chipboard)
The term covers a very wide range of boards made of a variety of source materials and adhesive fillers with widely-varying proper-

ties. Very little timber from environmentally-objectionable sources is now included in chipboard, but some of the adhesives used, especially those containing formaldehyde, call for special precautions in use to avoid health danger from gases emerging after installation should the boards become wet. It is desirable to enquire about the source of chipboard materials, as on occasions manufacturers have turned to areas such as the rain-forests of Papua New Guinea and the lower Amazon for materials. On the other hand, there is great scope for exploiting renewable coppicing and sustainable forestry for chipboards, as twigs can be used.

### Medium-Density Fibreboard
Now commonly used in the furniture industry as a substitute for both chipboard and solid timber in certain specialised contexts where the stablility of the material and the ease with which it can be machined to special shapes is valued. Tropical timber very rarely figures in the sources of raw material for such boards and its use can usually be precluded by a suitable specification clause.

### Asbestos Wallboard
Though asbestos poses no direct risk to health so long as it is completely encapsulated, the special difficulties which arise at the stage of demolition or during building alterations mean that alternatives should always be considered. Vermiculite and perlite boards are suitable replacements.

### Asbestos Cement Sheet
Alternative materials utilising other forms of fibre reinforcement, such as glass-reinforced cement (GRC), are now readily available and should always be preferred.

### Hardboard
The name refers to the characteristics of the board and not to the use of hardwood in its manufacture. Hardboard is an excellent and durable material if employed correctly in situations in which it can be protected from moisture and other causes of breakdown and distortion. However, it would be helpful if users could somehow

know if the wood from which hardboard is made was from a sustainable source.

**Lightweight Slabs**
Large slabs of compressed materials such as wood-wool (long shavings) and compressed straw are available for roof decking and partitioning applications. Wood-wool boards are also used for permanent formwork and as infill for cast concrete floors and roofs. Both materials are environmentally unobjectionable.

BRASS

An alloy of copper and zinc. Brass is an energy-hungry material in terms of its composition and manufacture. However, its durability is indefinite in most situations and it is easily and efficiently recycled.

If it contains less than 36 per cent zinc brass is ductile when cold and can be formed into complex shapes. Brass containing more than 36 per cent zinc is harder and stronger and machines easily. It does not corrode but if exposed to sea water the zinc may leach out; a process known as dezincification. This effect can be prevented to some extent with the addition of 1 per cent tin, and sometimes 0.05 per cent arsenic, when the material is described as Naval Brass.

BREEZE BLOCKS

A generic name used in the trade to describe blocks which incorporate lightweight aggregates, frequently of fly ash or other waste products, in which case they are from a renewable source and environmentally benign (see Blocks).

BRICKS

In this context, blocks made of burnt or fired clay, or of calcium silicate.

In building-industry jargon, a block which is small enough to be carried in one hand is referred to as a brick. Anything larger is either a block or a slab. Therefore small blocks of dense or lightweight concrete intended to be laid in mortar in walls in bonded patterns may strictly speaking come under this heading, but are not dealt with here (see Blocks). Clay bricks were first made in Britain by the Romans and then later reintroduced from the Low Countries and Germany in the

13th Century. The traditional landfill sites used in Britain for waste disposal came from pits left from clay extraction for bricks, but these are now difficult to use because of the areas becoming urbanised; people do not like to live near waste tips. The fundamental difference between bricks of clay or concrete and those made of calcium silicate (sandlimes or flintlimes) is that clay and concrete bricks tend to expand when new whilst calcium silicate bricks tend to contract.

Brick is ambivalent in environmental terms. When it is the vernacular material of the area, and easily available in the locality, its use could be acceptable to environmentalists, so long as good design practice aimed at durability is adopted. As it is so environment-destructive and energy-hungry, brick should be regarded as the exception rather than the rule, and when attractive and renewable local materials are available, such as sustainable timber, they should be preferred (see Vernacular Architecture and Construction).

The environmental situation concerning bricks is that on the one hand they are non-renewable; quarrying for the raw material destroys habitats and water tables, and manufacture and transport demand substantial quantities of energy. Brick-making is one of the energy-guzzling industries listed by the Energy Efficiency Office, and it conserves none of the energy it uses. Moreover, as with all ceramics, impurities burned off during the firing process give rise to undesirable substances in the flue gases, as experiments in recycling heat from such gases have indirectly indicated. Erosion of the material from which experimental heat-exchangers have been made has caused great difficulties in creating viable energy-saving systems in brick manufacture. It is true that such effects can be reduced by selecting the correct equipment, operating it with care, attending to the geometry of the exchanger, and maintaining it regularly. If recovering the waste gas can then be shown to be economic, it can be exploited successfully. But unfortunately brick manufacturers have so far demonstrated no anxiety to deal with this situation. On the positive side bricks and the structures in which they are incorporated are inherently durable, and involve little or no specific maintenance, and bricks can also be recycled if care is taken.

BUTYL

A relatively impermeable synthetic rubber manufactured by the copolymerisation of isobutylene and small quantities of isoprene. Non-renewable (see Rubber).

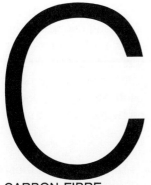

**CARBON FIBRE**

A synthetic material increasingly used as a form of fibre reinforcement in situations calling for a combination of light weight relative to high tensile strength and flexibility. Non-renewable (see Fibres).

**CARCINOGENS**

Apart from the recognised carcinogens such as coal tar and radiation, suspicion has recently fallen on electro-magnetic radiation from electricity pylons (see Radiation).

Another carcinogenic hazard has been found to be anilene and azo dyestuffs, and the plasticiser added to PVC plastic, such as clingfilms, which can migrate into the food which it wraps. A new type of plastic wrapping film without the plasticiser has now been developed.

**CARPETING**

(See Floorings)

**CEMENT AND CONCRETE**

Cement is usually made from a powder containing a mixture of calcium, silica, aluminium and other compounds, which vary according to the type and manufacturer. Cement extraction damages the environment, and its manufacture causes dust in the surrounding area.

As much as 5 per cent of the silica may be in the form of free silicon dioxide, which, breathed in, causes the lung damage known as silicosis. The calcium oxide (quicklime) content can cause severe skin burns, and the nose and throat can be damaged by the dry powder, while if it gets in the eyes it can result in permanent damage. Wet cement can painlessly burn the skin, resulting in damage which can require grafting.

Additives, such as calcium chloride to help setting speed or frost-proofing, and plasticisers, can cause skin damage, and dermatitis and eczema often result from contact. Plasterers suffer most, but other workers have also been affected. In north Kent a study of 600 cement workers found that their death rate from stomach cancer was 75 per cent higher than normal expectancy. Bearing all these facts in mind, it is worth checking that full precautions are taken by the manufacturer when cement is ordered in large quantities.

CERAMIC HOBS

A form of glass made of almost pure silica is used to create these cooking hobs, which will support very large temperature differentials within relatively small areas without distortion or fracturing. Various types exist, most being electrically heated. Production is energy-greedy, and the environmental attitude is that the same situation applies to hobs as to all other ceramic products: salvage, recycle and re-use wherever possible.

Electrically heated hobs either utilise infra-red elements, heating pans with ground bases by contact with the ceramic surface, or halogen elements, which heat to a greater extent by radiation. Ceramic hobs heated by gas have been developed, but have the disadvantage that the relative thermal inertia of the surface material tends to obviate the usual quick-response advantage of gas for cooking. Other types indirectly heat the contents of metal pans placed on the surface by electromagnetic radiation (see Kitchen Design).

CERAMICS

Fired clay material widely used in the building industry, destructive in manufacture, but durable in character. It comprises bricks, clay blocks, tiles made from terracotta or refined composite materials, and sanitary ware in glazed fireclay and vitreous china. The environmental approach to these products is to recycle and re-use such articles and use new ones as little as possible.

All ceramic manufacture involves raw materials which have to be dug from pits or quarries, destroying habitats and water tables, and causing direct visual and amenity damage to the local environment, not to mention air and noise pollution. Moreover, ceramic kilns emit flue gases which frequently contain toxic by-products and smell unpleasant. While in theory these waste gases could be recycled, it is a difficult process and little effort has been made in this direction. But, correctly utilised, ceramic products are almost indefinitely durable, and require very little maintenance. Ceramic panels and glazed brickwork are virtually self-cleaning and extremely resistant to atmospheric pollution. Architectural salvage is a highly profitable and fast-growing trade, and, as well as the sturdy Victorian sinks now growing alpines, an increasing number of people proudly display Victorian loos and bathroom fittings once again in use as good as ever. A few enlightened small builders, too, help their clients by inspecting the local builders' dump for discarded ceramic items for re-use. This tendency to salvage and re-use should extend to all ceramic products, whatever the age of the building being demolished. Builders' dumps should rapidly become a major local resource for all new buildings (see also Sanitary Ware).

CHALK                   (See Lime)

CHIMNEYS                (See Waste)

CHIPBOARD               (See Boards)

CHLORINE                A gas occurring in common salt in sea water and rocks, usually ob-tained by electrolysis of brine. It is used in the manufacture of bleaches, hydrochloric acid, in organic synthesis and in the purification of water. It can in this usage sometimes react with organic matter in the domestic water supply, creating harmful chemicals. On the Continent, some countries use ozonification to purify water rather than chlorine, for this reason. It is a powerful oxydising agent. and has been used as a non-persistent cloud gas in warfare because it has a destructive effect on the lungs and respiratory tract, and is highly lethal. Bleaching processes involv-ing chlorine give rise to dangerous dioxins. In general, the use of chlorine is discouraged by environmentalists (see also Water).

When burning domestic refuse in incinerators care must be taken not to include PVC, as when this is burnt – unless high-temperature industrial incineration is used – chlorine is released into the atmosphere and affects the ecosphere.

It has been discovered that the chlorine bleaching of such products as babies' nappies and sanitary tampons is potentially dangerous, as the process produces dioxins which could be harmful to the user. Creamy-coloured safe disposable nappies and tampons are now slowly coming into the shops, and all pure white paper products should be regarded with caution.

CLINKER               (See Aggregates)

COKE                  (See Blocks; Aggregates; Fuel)

CONCRETE              (See Cement and Concrete)

COOKERS               (See Kitchen Design)

COPPER                (See Metals)

CORK                  This is a renewable material, and environmentally benign. It is the bark of an evergreen oak, *Quercus suber*, and the stripping does not harm the tree; in ten years it is ready to be stripped again. The cells of the bark are air-filled, and can withstand pressures of up to 69,000 kilonewtons per square metre (10,000 lbs per square inch) without rupturing, returning to their former size when the pressure is withdrawn. Cork is light-weight, durable, non-flammable and excellent for flooring, insulation, bottle bungs and veneers. It is produced on the Iberian peninsula by small firms, and its use should be encouraged.

Cork trees are mature for stripping at 25 years. The first virgin bark is inferior, and used for composition materials. It is thought that the bark has developed in order for the trees to withstand the fires common in Mediterranean areas. No synthetic material has yet been devised which embodies all the characteristics of cork.

CREOSOTE

A coal-tar product, and therefore non-renewable. It is used as a wood preservative, but is toxic to plants when newly applied, and should therefore be used with care in gardens. Whenever possible, alternative preservatives and stains should be used.

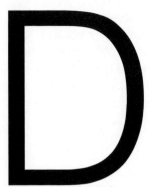

**DAMP-PROOFING**    (See Insulation)

**DETERGENTS**

Detergents are derivatives of petroleum. They do not form a scum when used in hard water. Soap is derived from a mixture of sodium salts of fatty acids, and is prepared by boiling fats and oils with an alkali. In hard water, soaps do cause scum to form, by precipitating calcium or magnesium salts, but soap does no harm to the environment. Detergents, on the other hand, contain phosphates which, when discharged into the water system, pollute the supply (see Water).

In the UK effluents containing soap, detergents and so-called biological washing powers are purified by the water authorities, to protect the environment and the water supply. This is a very expensive operation. In areas of particular sensitivity, such as the Norfolk Broads, in which the water should be free of the algae which develops from an excess of phosphates, a special stripping process is used to remove them.

**DIESEL**

It is widely believed that diesel-fuelled engines are more environment-friendly than their petrol-fuelled equivalents, but while reports from W. Germany tend to confirm this, others suggest there may be cancer risks involved.

Though lead additives are not required and emissions of gaseous pollutants are lower, even well-maintained diesel engines produce miniscule particles known as particulates, carriers of a group of chemical compounds known as polyaromatic hydrocarbons (PAHs), which may be carcinogens. Particulates in the atmosphere are also dangerous for people suffering from chronic breathing problems. They are generated even by diesel engines which are properly looked after, through incomplete combustion of fuel, incomplete combustion of lubricating oil and the formation of sulphate from the fuel sulphur. But when such engines are not properly and regularly maintained, toxic emissions rise sharply, frequently to the extent of breaking legal standards.

Should fuel prices rise substantially there is a possibility that the substitution of methanol for diesel could considerably reduce polluting emissions from these useful little engines. In due course it is hoped that legislation will bring about a reduction in the sulphur level in diesel fuel, and future regulations controlling emissions may well require the fitting of catalytic trap oxidisers to reduce particulates.

On construction sites diesel engines are often run inefficiently on tickover or low loads for long periods, which increases pollution. Environmental pressure is likely to lead increasingly to a switch to electric power for small plant.

| | |
|---|---|
| DISTRICT HEATING | (See Energy) |
| DOMESTIC KITCHEN | (See Kitchen Design) |
| DOORS | 1,420,000 doors, already made-up, were imported into Britain from tropical countries in 1984. Thus if doors were to be made up in Britain from European or sustainable forests a tremendous saving of tropical timber would be achieved. |
| DOUBLE GLAZING | (See Insulation) |
| DRAINS | (See Plumbing) |
| DRINKS DISPENSERS | The main area of concern about dispensers for hot and chilled drinks is that if they are not regularly maintained, and if any water filters fitted to them are not serviced regularly, there is a real risk of bacterial contamination. |

Voluntary codes covering maintenance standards are being operated by the relevant trade associations, but it is possible that in the aftermath of water privatisation new water regulations will impose more stringent standards upon those supplying and maintaining equipment which dispenses drinking water.

DUCTED AIR

Various ducted air systems have been devised for introducing fresh air into buildings with or without air-conditioning. From the environmental point of view, the mechanical-ventilation system is the most desirable, as no CFC-using air-conditioning is employed. Fresh air is ducted in during warm weather, and the air is warmed in winter (see Appendix).

DYES

(See Pigments and Dyes)

ECO-
ARCHITECTURE

The following principles are suggested to form the basis of a new and ecologically-harmonious attitude to architecture.

1   It is always preferable to re-use, adapt or extend an existing structure rather than demolish or re-build.

2   Take into account, when studying the site, the built environment; its history and purpose; local micro-climates and the prevailing winds and weather patterns of the area; solar orientation; use of vernacular materials (low transport costs are an environmental gain); respect for local vernacular design and form.

3   Provide a friendly and efficient environment. This is the first duty when designing the form and function of any structure, new, adapted or rebuilt; comfort for those who will be using it and sharing the space which it occupies. Environmentalists contend that this is more important than the role of the building as a statement about its owner or designer.

4   Respect local traditions in materials and design. Not only did they arise from practical experience over the centuries of what works well in the area, it was the respect of the past generation of designers that created the harmony which is now so admired in our towns and villages. Avoid materials from non-renewable sources, and materials which cannot be recycled.

5   Design the building as a total ecosystem. Energy use, water and the production of waste are fundamental functions. Incorporate energy-saving techniques, methods of conserving water and recycling of waste. A basic Green principle is that waste is

processed at the source, by separation and recycling, or by incinerating for heating purposes, that which cannot be recycled.

6    Utilise surface finishes inside and outside the building which do not need regular renewal or refurbishment. Natural surfaces, self-cleaning materials, tiles that can be cleaned indefinitely, and good textiles with a very long life are in the long run more economical than cheaper alternatives.

7    Use natural ventilation, unless there are specialist needs, openable windows or ducted air (see Air-conditioning).

8    Build to last at least 100 years. All building involves at least some environmental destruction, but the impact can be minimised by providing structures which will be observed with pleasure by posterity.

Changes in the structure of the building industry in recent years have altered the role of the designer and specifier, whether it be the architect, interior designer or building engineer. The specialist professional has all but disappeared, to be replaced by technicians concerned with cost, quality and performance guarantees. In this change, the wider issues of beauty, the social roles of buildings, and the environmental impact of structures, the materials of which they are made on the animate and inanimate surroundings, have become at best secondary considerations. They have come to be seen, if they are seen at all, as extraneous matters to be stuck onto the basic concept. The Green view is that each construction should be conceived as an organic whole, functioning as such, and in harmony with all around it.

The recycling of previous building materials is another major Green consideration. Enlightened builders are turning more and more to local building dumps for discarded materials. The old-fashioned metal bath, for example, reycled and repainted, is better both environmentally and practically than a newly-made plastic one. It is to be hoped that the small dumps which already exist will increasingly be developed into larger depots for discards from demolished commercial buildings, especially the glass and other recyclable artefacts.

It is startling to discover how few modern office buildings have taken into account the actual use and comfort of the staff who will be working within. Brokers in the new Lloyd's Building in the City of London, for example, complain that their old building was a more convenient shape for their working pattern. Most of the people in offices inspired by the Mies van der Rohe school have had to shield themselves by some device stuck over the windows. The most successful architectural design flows from consideration of the patterns of functioning, and comfort through all seasons, of the users, combined with the considerations contained in the first principle above.

Exciting new fields of design are opened up in the innovative use of natural materials as slate, timber from sustainable sources, leather, cork, linoleum and the renewable textiles. It is also preferable to use local flint or brick, which will blend in with past structures, than to import such environmentally-undesirable materials as concrete. Possibly new and attractive materials will be devised in the future from demolition rubble and other waste.

Unfortunately this is not current thinking. We are still in the age of 'shelf-life' and 'built-in obsolescence'. The oncoming Green era demands a radical transformation of thought, taking account of hidden ecological costs and returning to the craft concept, that everything worth making at all is worth making to last for ever. This offers a new challenge to designers of structures and the materials of which they are made to create new products without destroying the world about us in the process.

ELECTRICITY          (See Energy)

ENERGY               Defined as the capacity of a system to do work. All use of energy exploits the environment in some way, but some sources are renewable and others are not. These are tabulated overleaf.

In the case of coal some progress has been made on the environmental front: see Fuel.

The Commission of the European Community set up an Energy Demonstration Programme in 1978 in order to promote new technologies in energy saving, alternative energy, hydrocarbon

| Renewable | Non-renewable |
|---|---|
| Biomass | Coal (but see below) |
| CHP | Coal derivatives |
| Geotherm | Natural gas |
| Hydro | Oil |
| Methane from biomass | Peat |
| Methane from landfill | Propane |
| Solar | Wood (from non-sustainable forest) |
| Waste burning | |
| Wave power | |
| Wind | |
| Wood (from sustainable forest) | |

*Other*
Combined heat and power (District Heating)

substitution and liquefaction and the gasification of solid fuels. In renewable energy the Commission supports projects in the solar, wind, geothermal, hydropower and biomass sectors (See Appendix).

Environmentally-aware designers plan the energy layout for the needs and use of the specific building under consideration. The options include the possibility of using combined heat and power (district heating); solar power; wind-power, biogas from a methane source such as sewage (see Waste); or waste incineration (see Waste). But in all cases insulation is necessary for energy conservation.

**Combined Heat and Power (CHP)**
In a normal power station, 65 per cent of the initial primary energy is lost, much of it in the form of water. CHP is a method of recovering at least some of this energy, and micro-CHP 'packages' are now available for smaller installations. These have electrical outputs of up to 160 kW, with a thermal output two or three times that figure. The 1983 Energy Act required electricity boards to offer to purchase electricity produced by private generators with their own CHP systems if this is practicable, and to adopt and support such

systems. Appropriate tariffs have been published. New legislation may change this situation. The relatively low cost of small CHP units and their heat and electrical output renders them suitable for use in hotels, hospitals, universities, residential homes, swimming pools and similar-sized projects (see Appendix).

Designs for minimum-energy consumption in buildings are beginning to appear, and it is increasingly realised that energy-greedy buildings are out of date. False ceilings, for example, inhibit proper energy conservation, and designers seeking to avoid energy loss now expose the concrete ceiling slab so that the heat which rises during the day will be absorbed by the structure and stored. We can control the energy input and the energy losses of any building by such things as the overall form, the construction of the external walls, insulation, window size, shading, etc. Victorian buildings, built as they are with solid walls, have high thermal capacity and a potential for energy conservation, which can be enhanced by insulation. Also, given their 'normal' window sizes, they present no problems of solar overheating. In addition, their solid walls work well for other forms of environmental filtering, and offer excellent sound insulation between rooms (see also Air-conditioning; Fuel).

An example is the GEV building in Cologne, which uses 50 per cent of the electricity and 8 per cent of the heat that is consumed in any of the thirty-two earlier-style *burolandschaft* offices in the area.

A possible outcome of electric power privatisation is the development of small private power generation plants linked to industrial and commercial complexes, which sell excess production to the grid and call upon the grid for supplies in the event of breakdown or overload. Most of these are likely to be coal fired and there is a mounting controversy over whether they will tend to buy cheap imported coal, especially that now being imported from South Africa, in relatively low-tech plants, which will be difficult to upgrade as emissions standards become stricter, or adopt the latest British Coal fluidised-bed technology, which is relatively expensive to install but efficient and eco-friendly (see Fuel).

# F

| | |
|---|---|
| FABRICS | (See Textiles) |
| FELT | (See Fibres) |
| FENCING | This is now available from sustainable wood sources, such as chestnut palings from coppicing. From a horticultural point of view, perforated fencing is best, because a fence which filters wind is less destructive to the plants it is intended to shelter than a solid one, which creates destructive down-draughts. |
| FIBREBOARD | (See Boards) |
| FIBRES | Natural and man-made hair-like structures widely used in building and textiles. |

**Metal/Mineral**
All metal fibres cause dust during manufacture which, breathed in, can cause a type of silicosis. Steel and asbestos fibres are used in Portland cement and reinforced concrete. Asbestos fibres are also mixed into bituminous products. Rockwool, a fibrous material produced by heating and spinning rock, is used in reinforced composites and for thermal insulation. Slag wool is a similar material, spun from molten blast-furnace slag, and therefore renewable and environmentally beneficent. Carbon fibres, which are non-renewable, are now frequently used in a variety of composite materials.

Workers in dusty industries suffer a much higher incidence than the norm of bronchitis, stomach and lung cancer, heart disease and digestive troubles. The mucus coating of the air tubes in the lungs can trap larger fibres and gradually expel them, but not the fine particles. The fibres used to make fibreglass, for example, are too thick to be breathed into the lungs, though heavy concentrations of the dust cause skin, throat and chest complaints. It would be helpful if all intending purchasers of materials containing mineral fibres enquired of the manufacturers whether full protective measures were taken to obviate the ingestion of dust. The manufacturers of all products that contain glass, ceramic or rock fibres should be using the same safeguards as for asbestos unless the processes are proved to be safe (see Glass Fibre; Insulation).

**Natural**

Vegetable and animal fibres, such as wood, hessian, sisal, coir, jute cloth and animal hair, are used in various reinforced composites. All these, if the wood is from sustainable forestry, are renewable and therefore environmentally beneficent.

Extremely fine filaments of carbon are produced as carbon fibres to reinforce components of jet engines; carbon is regarded as a non-metallic element (see also Asbestos; Textiles).

FIBROUS PLASTER        (See Plaster)

FINISHES        These come broadly into two categories – protective and decorative. Protection techniques aimed at prolonging the life of materials and structures are now receiving increased attention, partly because this may be the only way in which many relatively modern materials can challenge the inherent longevity of traditional alternatives. In neither case is there yet much evidence of a trend towards the use of alternative environment-friendly materials. For instance, one would consider that wallpaper would be an ideal application for recycled paper but none is so far available. There are now some brands of paint available incorporating vegetable oils rather than modern acrylics, which are highly polluting in manufacture.

Many materials, especially boards and panels, can now be obtained ready-finished, and this increases the attraction of dry-liner construction techniques, minimising the use of environmentally-undesirable materials which involve mining and quarrying (see Paint).

## FLOORINGS

It is true of many building materials that the only advantage offered by the newer high-tech products, which are almost entirely derived from non-renewable raw materials, is that they are cheaper. This is mainly because synthetics are manufactured in bulk at low labour cost and under close control. However, the processing of renewable materials such as wool, cotton, jute and other plant fibres involves more labour, transport over greater distances and more expensive processing, because of the inherent uncertainties of dealing with natural materials. On the other hand, as discussed elsewhere, all non-renewables involve hidden costs and so this has to be the basis of assessing the Greenness of alternative flooring materials. Moreover, many high-tech products are not built to last, thus proving more expensive in the long run. Floors of solid wood, parquet, cork tiles, solid stone, brick and possibly linoleum, are potentially recyclable, but few others can be re-used. (*See table opposite.*)

## FOAM

Plastic foams, non-renewable, fall into two categories:

*Rigid foam* (polystyrene) is frequently used for cavity insulation in new buildings, because blocks can be purchased with it already applied. Once environmentally-undesirable because CFCs were used in its production, it is now widely available CFC-free.

*Flexible foam* (polyurethane) is widely used in upholstering furniture. In February 1989 this highly flammable foam will become illegal in furniture in the UK but can still legally be used in insulation, and is occasionally so used by do-it-yourself practitioners. Such use is better avoided. Rockwool is an alternative, and is becoming the preferred choice, for example, around hot-water cylinders (see also Plastics).

## FOOD

Environmentalists wish to see a swing back towards greater use of fresh food. This will involve the rediscovery of the ventilated

| Material | Source type | Durability | Notes |
|---|---|---|---|
| Asphalt | Renewable | Long life | Renewable if lake asphalt |
| Brick | Non-renewable | Indefinite | Recycling potential |
| Carpet – wool | Renewable | Long life | |
| synthetic | Non-renewable | Potential long life | Very variable performance |
| Cement | Non-renewable | Long life | Correct maintenance essential |
| Ceramic tiles | Non-renewable | Long life | Some recycling potential |
| Chipboard | Renewable | Medium life | Protection essential |
| Cork | Renewable | Long life | |
| Linoleum | Renewable | Long life | Traditional material reborn |
| Plywood and composites | Renewable | Long life | See notes on wood floors |
| Parquet | Renewable? | Long life | Recyclable. See wood floors |
| Rubber (butyl) | Non-renewable | Medium life | Sensible application of synthetic material |
| Stone (solid) | Non-renewable | Indefinite | Recycling potential |
| Terrazzo and granolithic | Non-renewable | Indefinite | Efficient use of raw material |
| Vinyl and composites | Non-renewable | Medium life | Consider linoleum as an alternative |
| Wood (hard) | Renewable | Long life | Recycling potential, but avoid tropical timbers |
| Wood (soft) | Renewable | Medium life | Recycling potential. Life can be extended by good design and maintenance |

larder, in which our forebears kept eggs, cheese, vegetables and fruit quite successfully. Meat was put in its coolest corner with a metal mesh guard over it to keep out flies. Milk and butter were there in water-coolers. While a small fridge is a useful thing in hot weather, it is by no means the universal need we have come to imagine. Neither is the freezer. Although it helps us to be able to buy in bulk, and save a glut of vegetables, it is also energy-consuming, and Greens strive to find other answers to these needs.

In earlier days diet was, in fact, more varied, as we took advantage of natural seasonal food gluts, although quite a lot was preserved and bottled. More imagination was applied then to the culinary use of native vegetables and other crops. *Petit pois* in mid-winter are not Green! The widespread adoption of fridges and freezers as a method of preserving foods has discouraged diversity; discouraged the use of seasonally available, and therefore cheaper, foods; encouraged the development of standardised food products and, oddly enough, encouraged greater use of preservatives and techniques, such as irradiation, to increase 'shelf life'. Total dependence on fridges and freezers leads inevitably to boring, repetitive, less nutritious eating. As a means to secure cheap food it is, in the end, self-defeating. And a generation has grown up which is helpless without the giant fridge in the kitchen (see also Kitchen Design).

FUEL

Coal (but see below), oil, paraffin, propane gas and peat are non-renewable. Wood from a renewable source is a relatively environmentally benign fuel but releases carbon back into the atmosphere, contributing to the greenhouse effect. Methane gas is renewable when produced from waste or biomass, but contributes in a small way to the greenhouse effect (see Waste; Biofuel).

The extraction of peat accounts for a large proportion of the 98 per cent of our wetlands now lost in Britain, along with all the wildlife, often rare, they contained. Bark chippings and other renewable substitutes for peat should be used wherever possible.

*Coal* is an ambivalent fuel from the environmental angle, depending on how it is exploited.

On the one hand it is not renewable; when obtained by open-cast mining its extraction totally destroys wildlife habitats and the water table, and unless expensive equipment is installed its combustion is partly responsible for acid rain. On the other hand, coal is a valuable standby while steps are taken to conserve the energy lost in our present methods of energy production and use, and the waste from coal extraction, if trouble is taken, can be rendered reusable, unlike the waste created by nuclear power stations. Moreover, a new technique in coal processing has been developed: fluidised-bed combustion, which has great environmental advantages. All types of coal, even poor shales, can be used (see also Waste); it reduces or even prevents the emission of sulphur dioxide (valuable for coal which has a high sulphur-dioxide content); and in addition there is no erosion or corrosion of the construction equipment; there are low emissions of deposit-forming materials, and the boilers used are smaller and cheaper (see Appendix). Moreover, waste disposal pellets produced from municipal waste processing can be mixed with coal or used alone on fluidised beds.

The £100-million pioneer fluidised-bed plant, at Grimethorpe, in Yorkshire, has reached the stage of the last, crucial experiment to demonstrate the feasibility of this new technique. The new Slough Industrial Estate is being powered by coal used in a Green manner, with a fluidised-bed combined heat and power system, an example to be followed up and down the country, we hope.

Smokeless fuel produces certain undesirable effects when it is being produced from coal. A dust is given off which has caused complaints from people living near smokeless fuel factories, and there is evidence of high local incidence of bronchial disease in such areas (see also Energy).

Fly-ash from coal-burning power stations is used to make light-weight concrete blocks which should be encouraged in house-building; they have excellent thermal insulation properties and are a good example of re-using waste.

*Methane Gas* is a fuel which is renewable when it is produced by decaying organic matter. Like butane and propane, it occurs naturally in oil wells (Baku, Pittsburgh, the Crimea and other places), but all three are then non-renewable, although there are large reserves. The important point about methane is that it becomes renewable when it is produced from biomass or waste in-filling. It can then be exploited to heat buildings if the necessary equipment is installed (see Waste). It does contribute in a small way to the greenhouse effect.

Methane produced by the world's constantly growing population of herbivores is also contributing to the greenhouse effect, and there is a colourful theory that this was what did away with the dinosaurs! Methane can be created from biomass by feeding fast-rotting greenstuff, farmed for the purpose, into digesters. This is a possible Green replacement for oil as a feedstock for a variety of processes, including the manufacture of plastics (see Appendix).

FURNISHING
FABRICS

(See Textiles)

FURNITURE

The Green trend is to revert to traditional framed construction, greater use of solid timber, and upholstery systems which can be renewed non-destructively. The challenge to designers is to create modern forms which also offer the option of recycling when the first use is over. There is no reason, for example, why furniture manufactured from finished chipboard should not have an indefinite life. Longevity depends as much on form, finishes and the methods of assembly employed as on the material used in such cases.

In retail jargon, furniture is referred to as a consumer durable, but design trends since World War II have meant that it has become quite the opposite. Both domestically and commercially it has increasingly been regarded as a fashion product, all too often made of materials, such as veneered or coated chipboards and plastics, which have a limited lifespan.

GAS                  (See Energy; Waste)

GLASS          Glass is created by the fusion of sand (silica) with lime and soda or potash, with the addition of other metallic oxides. Limestone is used in this process. Both sand and limestone must be extracted from the earth – sea-sand will not do – an environmentally-destructive process. The same remarks on the destruction of the environment apply as in the extraction of aggregates. The manufacturers are reluctant to provide figures on the energy cost during production. Sheet or plate glass is rarely produced now, the more economical float process is used for this type of glass.

All glass can in theory be recycled, if it is separated from other materials. If, for example, it is removed pane by pane from buildings due to be demolished it can be re-used. Manufacturers recycle their own cullet when making glass; all glass returned to bottle banks is recycled by bottle manufacturers.

Glass manufacture is one of the 'high-temperature process industries' listed by the Energy Efficiency Office, and loses heat as hot gases. Although these gases are contaminated to some extent, careful selection of the right equipment and good maintenance could still result in the recovery of some of this lost energy. The waste product from glass manufacture consists of glassy blocks and the clinker from old kilns. Now that modern glass production uses the float process, sand is no longer a waste product. The large lumps of glassy clinker are sometimes sold to sculptors for re-use.

In design, the characteristics of glass need fully to be understood. It has certain properties which affect its performance in the spectrum of solar radiation. Some of the energy which strikes it goes straight through, some is reflected and some is absorbed, including the longer infra-red rays, so that the glass warms up. The shorter infra-red rays go through and strike objects inside the building, warming them up. Along with warmth from the glass itself, the room inside warms up as well. Venetian blinds have no effect on this process. Bronze glass reflects rather more, but absorbs more solar energy, half of which tends to be radiated back into the inner space. Mirrored glass, if thick silvering is used, inhibits the view and reflects solar heat outward. Surveys of office users in Victorian buildings with windows, as against those working in glass-walled buildings, show that the former are more comfortable for those within (see Appendix).

An environmental advantage of glass as a bottling material is that it can be sterilised and re-used. In 1972 the State of Oregon in the US passed a bill requiring all glass drinks containers to carry a deposit and be returnable. There is no reason why the British Government should not follow suit.

GLASS FIBRE

Usually fine filaments of glass woven into a cloth and impregnated with synthetic resins, therefore being composed of both glass and plastic. Glass-reinforced plastic (GRP) is plastic material reinforced with glass fibres.

Glass fibre is not completely hazard-free in its manufacture. The strands mostly have a diameter of around 13 microns, which is too thick to be breathed into the lungs, but it is important that workers exposed to heavy concentrations of dust from the process should be protected, as they have been found to experience skin, throat and chest complaints. All fibres cause dust in their manufacture (see Fibres), and dust from such fibres should be treated with the same precautions as for asbestos production. If intending purchasers of insulation material containing fibres enquired as to these precautions of the manufacturers, no doubt progress towards safety in processing would be encouraged.

All materials made up from glass fibres and plastics are extremely strong, lightweight and corrosion-resistant. Various mixtures are used in boats, vehicle bodies, glass fibre-reinforced cement (GRC), and insulation. While these are non-renewable and there is some environmental damage in the extraction of the raw material and in manufacture (see Glass), they are to be preferred over more destructive materials. They are inert, and superior to plastic foams for insulation because they are not flammable (see Insulation).

GLUES            (See Adhesives)

GRANITE          Hard rock used for chippings, kerbs, sett paving, setts, etc. Granite is increasingly used as a sheet cladding for the exteriors of commercial and industrial buildings because it is very resistant to almost all forms of environmental degradation and requires little maintenance. In this context the material has an indefinite lifespan, the limit usually being the underlying structure and method of panel attachment chosen. If properly handled, therefore, it can be recycled indefinitely (see Stone).

GRAPHITE         Naturally occurring form of carbon, found in black, soft masses or occasionally as crystals. Used in black lead, plumbago (in crucibles) and, finely ground, added to some oils. Non-renewable.

GRAVEL           (See Aggregates)

GUTTERS          An increasing number of materials are now being used to form guttering and each has its environmental advantages and disadvantages. (*See table overleaf.*)

GYPSUM           (See Finishes)

| Material | Comments |
| --- | --- |
| Aluminium | Lightweight and therefore easy to handle but a non-renewable, high-energy material with little potential for recycling other than as scrap. Low maintenance requirement. |
| Asbestos cement | Relatively little used now as there are more attractive alternatives. |
| Cast iron | Attractive traditional material in vernacular situations, where the visual character it takes on with age will be regarded as an advantage. Requires more maintenance than most modern alternatives and needs stronger fixings due to weight. |
| Plastics | A variety of plastics are now used for guttering and have the advantage of being self-finished. In long runs allowance must be made for expansion and contraction if distortion is to be avoided. Light weight and inherently low maintenance are considerable advantages. Most traditional styles can now be matched. |
| Lead | The only material, apart possibly from copper, which can be made to produce a curved gutter. The use of lead is essential in some vernacular situations, but degradation by acid rain is a problem to be borne in mind (see Acid Rain). |

# H

HAIR            (See Fibres)

HALOGEN         (See Kitchen Design)

HEAVY METALS    (See Metals)

HARDWOODS       (See Wood)

HEATING         (See Fuel)

**I**

**IMPREGNATION, TIMBER**

Timber is treated before installation in structures in order to prevent insect and fungal attack, and to increase its resistance to moisture and encourage durability. Our forefathers used well-seasoned oak, or other material suitable to the need, and some of these ancient timbers are now like iron and even re-usable, but such material is no longer easily available. Softwoods in particular are held to need preservatives. Wildlife organisations will generally supply details of preservatives to be preferred in order that bats, for example, suffer no harm in attic roosts. The ingredients of recommended preservatives are permethrin, boron compounds and acypetacs zinc. These are also recommended from the point of view of the health of people in the building (see Preservatives; Pesticides; and see Timber Treatment for a reassessment of the role of chemical treatment).

**INSECTICIDES**

(See Preservatives)

**INSULATION**

A major means of conserving energy. It has been calculated that in a conventional house, a third of its heat is lost through the roof, a quarter through the walls, a fifth through the floor and usually more still from draughts. Some genuinely energy-efficient houses have now been built (see Appendix), with effectively-insulated floors, walls and ceilings, window draughts obviated by secondary glazing, draught-proofing round doors and a draught-proof letter-box. The best material to use from an environmental point of view for insulation in buildings, especially lofts, is glass fibre, because it is not flammable (see Glass Fibre).

Many insulating materials cause dust in their manufacture (see Glass Fibre). If intending purchasers of material containing metal fibres enquired as to precautions for the workers during their manufacture, progress towards safety would be encouraged.

While cavity walls help with insulation from cold and sound, they lose heat through air convection, and therefore should contain insulation in the cavity. This can be injected into existing cavity walls, but precautions should be taken with flammable foam. In lofts a 100 mm layer of insulation will pay for itself in three years. In new houses double-glazing can be installed; secondary glazing usually proves satisfactory in dwellings already built.

It is necessary to differentiate between insulation against noise (see Noise) and thermal insulation. The positioning of secondary glazing is different for sound, and a compromise has to be made depending upon the needs of the building. Satisfactory sound insulation can require 100 mm or more between panes, whereas the ideal gap for thermal insulation is 20mm, and a balance has to be drawn depending upon the circumstances. Sometimes triple-glazing is necessary.

New insulation standards were laid down by the Government in the summer of 1989.

IRON

Although non-renewable, cast and malleable iron are highly durable materials, tolerant of lack of attention and with inherently-low maintenance requirements. Once produced, they are therefore low-energy metals, and can also be recycled efficiently. It follows that there are many situations in which these materials should be considered as an alternative to modern metals, though this may entail the acceptance of possible disadvantages in less flexible design and more site handling. Genuine wrought iron has many of the same advantages, and is being manufactured again in common trade sizes at the Ironbridge Museum in Shropshire.

Goods and fittings of cast or mild steel are often offered, and described, as iron. It is necessary therefore to check so as to be absolutely sure (see Metals).

# K

## KITCHEN DESIGN

Green thinking calls for re-learning the arts of cookery with fresh, seasonal produce, and low-energy methods of storing foods without the use of artificial preservatives. One consequence will be the return of the ventilated larder, which was a casualty of the arrival of 'system kitchen' design thinking in the late 1950s. Increased use of foods dried by low-tech methods, already commonplace with spices, pulses and rice, and with many other foods in Third World countries, will also increase.

From the food we choose to buy and the way we store it to the specification of the furniture and appliances and the way we handle waste products, every aspect of kitchen design has environmental implications. As already mentioned (see Food), there has been a trend over the past two or three decades away from using fresh, mainly seasonal and native foods towards year-round universal food products which inevitably call for ever greater use of refrigeration and freezing, not to mention other preservative techniques involving anything from chemicals and coatings to irradiation, as well as international transport and more intensive agriculture. One result is less variety in everyday food, because to date the trend towards greater diversity illustrated on bookshop shelves and television programmes has been a lesser influence than the convenience of supermarket alternatives. Another is that almost all the foods we eat are now contaminated to a greater or lesser extent with a range of pesticides and other substances which contribute nothing to their positive nutritional value.

Though energy use in cookery is minor compared with that employed for space heating, gas as a fuel has a clear cost advantage over electricity. This is true even when such high-efficiency techniques as microwave cookery are used. However, it is worth reflecting that you save more energy by boiling the amount of water you actually want in an electric kettle than by heating up a full kettle on a gas stove when all you need is enough to fill a small teapot.

Efficient domestic use of energy, in this as in other ways, depends at least as much on people and the way they live as on technical considerations. For instance, the cheapest generally-available type of cooker to run is, in theory, an Aga. However, this is only true if you have use for the constant heat which it offers, even outside the normal space-heating season. The Green approach is therefore to use the fuel which is most convenient, but to use it efficiently, rather than to attempt to force people to change what amount to cultural patterns.

In the case of kitchen furniture, the situation is fairly clear. Almost all current kitchen units are designed for a known and limited target life, and cannot be recycled in any useful form when that life is over. In fact, kitchen furniture is increasingly being marketed as a fashion item.

The Green approach is to revert to traditional construction and materials, somewhat in line with the current fashion trend towards individual free-standing furniture elements. Specifically, the Green kitchen would therefore not include articulated system hinges or plastic-coated metal drawer runners, as all of these have limited efficient working lives and cannot be replaced satisfactorily. Instead, traditional brass or non-ferrous butt hinges and wood-on-wood drawer runners are to be preferred.

At first sight this would seem to preclude factory mass-production, but as fashions swing towards traditional furniture, methods are being found to achieve the same manufacturing efficiencies using traditional components and cabinet-making methods. In any case the cost advantage to the consumer which panel-based mass production of kitchen units is supposed to offer has largely been eliminated by current marketing methods, which interpose considerable distribution costs between factories and end-users.

Some of the materials used in kitchen furniture illustrate the conflicts which can arise between different strands of the environmental movement. Chipboard, for instance, is suggested by some to be an eco-virtuous material because it is made from northern softwoods, whereas most of the plywood used in the furniture and building trades in Britain is still made of tropical hardwoods endangered by lack of proper forest management practices. Others would argue that the spruce monoculture which is behind the chipboard industry in most parts of Europe is itself environmentally-undesirable. Moreover, chipboard factories introduce the inevitable pollution inherent in all intensive industrial activity to areas often of outstanding natural beauty. Then again, both chipboard and the plastic laminates which are the basis of today's kitchens utilise formaldehyde, which is a by-product of meat-industry waste. Urea formaldehyde and similar glues are the main binders used in making chipboard, and Melamine formaldehyde is used to surface high-pressure laminates for working surfaces and to coat chipboard for interiors and shelves. It is unlikely that many vegetarians realise that they are slicing their eggs on a material which started life as waste bones, hides and offal, but on the other hand others might regard this as an example of sensible use of waste products.

The choice of the wood used in kitchen furniture is also a complicated question. Generally speaking, environmentalists seek to use English, European or American hardwoods, unless they are sure that the source of the wood is from sustainable forests (see Appendix).

Tropical hardwoods are not often used in the European-made kitchen furniture currently available, except for Italian and Spanish products. Their use can easily be avoided in any case by specifying wood from Europe or North America.

Working surfaces are another matter. In the past, teak was widely regarded as the supreme working surface material. Most teak comes from Indonesia, where the government has the benefit of mature teak plantations in Java set down by the Dutch at the turn of the century. They urgently need the hard currency which the sale of this wood can bring them, and have set up a scheme for replanting the mature trees which they are felling. However, they wish to convert timber to finished sizes in Java, thus increasing their share of the value added in the total production process, and British companies whose production systems, and profitability, are geared to handling logs, have been slow to accept this new approach. Worktops of Java Teak, accompanied by a certificate of Green origin, are now available again in Britain (see Appendix), and the company involved is also offering sycamore and rock maple from temperate forest sources mainly in North America, as alternatives. But because the finishing is done in Java the Indonesians have found very few outlets in the developed countries for prepared Java Teak, so they are still being forced to export log, timber and other undesirable wood products to Japan and North America. In the meantime, efforts to combat this trade are actually preventing proper recognition of the positive alternatives.

A genuinely threatened tropical hardwood, iroko, has come into wide use in commercial catering, in particular because it can be obtained in very wide boards to produce seamless preparation blocks. Though it has to be said that the scale of use of iroko for working surfaces is miniscule compared with its use in architectural joinery, it is now impossible to get this wood from most African countries where it was hitherto available, and there are no sustainably managed forests producing it, so that it is likely to disappear in the near future.

Where items other than furniture are concerned, Green preoccupations about avoiding high-tech materials and manufacturing processes have made little impact as yet. Stainless steel is still the main material for sinks and taps, and other plumbing fittings are made almost exclusively of brass and finished by plating or plastic coating. Alternatives are being developed, but it will be some years before they are economically competitive with current products.

For example, glazed fireclay sinks modelled on Victorian designs are now available again. These are made from a material which is an otherwise waste product of coal-mining, and the glazing and firing processes involved are all relatively low-tech by ceramics standards. Glazed fireclay is an immensely tough material which resists absolutely all of the acids, caustics and cleaning materials which arise in domestic kitchens, unlike either stainless steel or the alternative composites or plastics now widely in use. However, costs are generally far higher than those for equivalent stainless steel sinks, and the nature of the manufacturing process is such that substantial economies of scale are not possible.

Water is used at some stage in virtually every process in the kitchen (see Water for notes on drinking water purity and water filters, on economy measures and methods of disposal).

Domestic waste can now largely be recycled even in rural areas, but the effectiveness of such schemes depends on not allowing kitchen wastes to become mixed up in the first place. Waste therefore needs to be separated as it is produced, and in response to this requirement many kitchen manufacturers are now able to incorporate compartmented 'ecobins' into their furniture.

This approach is a total switch from the wider adoption of sink waste disposers which was being forecast only a few years ago within the trade, or the now-commonplace 'swing bin' lined with a catch-all plastic bag. In future, kitchens will increasingly incorporate either multi-compartment bins or alternatively two or three separate containers for different types of waste. The main categories are compostable food residues, either for your own compost heap or that of your neighbour; metals; glass; paper and plastics. Considerable pressures are being put on members of parliament to obtain legislation for the proper disposal of waste, which in itself is a precious resource (see also Slow Cooking).

# L

**LAMINATES**

Melamine formaldehyde, which is combined with Kraft paper to form most high-pressure laminates, is a by-product of meat production and therefore an eco-friendly use of slaughterhouse wastes. Such laminates are now widely used both for domestic furniture and as architectural surface claddings (see Plastics; Paper; Wood).

**LAND DERELICTION**

Since the industrial revolution an increasing area of derelict land has been created by various activities: brick-making, iron and steel production, stone quarrying, open-cast coal-mining, and the extraction of tin, china clay, lead, slate, sand and gravel. During this activity all wild-life habitats and water tables and springs were destroyed. A recent report by the Department of the Environment stated that in England and Wales there are 46,500 hectares (115,000 acres) of such land, including spoil-heaps, excavations and borrow pits. Ironically, such areas are often rehabilitated for agricultural use by, among other processes, applying a top dressing of limestone, the extraction of which itself involves total land destruction. A new speciality is therefore emerging: expertise in assessing and rehabilitating derelict areas in an environmentally-positive form. The knowledge required is wide-ranging, and includes soil ecology, land drainage, worm populating, entomology, soil aeration and land cultivation.

**LAUNDERING**

Green thinking has had a more direct impact on the equipment and materials used for domestic laundering than almost any other area of the home. Practically everything used can now be obtained in an eco-virtuous form.

German manufacturers of laundering equipment in particular, in response to Green political pressures in that country, have drastically reduced energy and water use by their machines during the past decade and worked closely with makers of environment-friendly detergents to improve efficiency in use and largely obviate the need for the enzymes, softeners and brighteners which are such a feature of most branded detergent products at present. More efficient designs of dryers are also emerging, mostly involving recycling of the heated air rather than venting it out of the building. There is also a trend towards off-peak laundering, to take advantage of night-time lower power costs. The likely installation of water meters and rising cost of water are also bringing a demand for machines which recycle the water used in washing machines. A number of people now do this themselves by hand.

LEAD

(See Metals; Paint; Acid Rain)

LEATHER

All leather is made from animal hides or skins, and leather is therefore a renewable resource so long as cattle continue to be exploited by human beings.

The tanning of leather includes treatment with salt, lime, solvents and chemicals including chromium III sulphate. Originally natural tannins were used: polyphenolic plant extracts akin to tea, which were therefore renewable. Further processes use both natural oils, which are renewable, and gluteraldehyde, dyes and bleaches, which are not. In the days of natural tannins, the chemical-free waste material from boot and shoe factories was sought after for composting as a garden fertiliser, and was thus recycled.

LIGHTING

New low-energy lighting systems are now reaching the market-place almost every week. There is copious technical information available, both about the systems themselves and about relating their energy-use to alternative situations, and we shall not cover the ground again here. But very little information is available on the hidden costs to the environment involved in the materials and manufacture of luminaires (light fittings) or light sources, making it impossible to put systems into perspective from a Green point of view, and the situation is so fluid that at this stage enquiries on that angle are best made by the designer or other potential user direct to the manufacturer. In addition, the actual use of light in new buildings has up to now been, and largely continues to be, wasteful and user-unfriendly, and Green thinking on this subject is unambiguous.

Offices and factories use 80 per cent of the energy consumed by lighting. Greens recognise that reductions in energy use can be achieved by many means other than high-tech development. It cannot be environmentally desirable to design a building in which perhaps thousands of luminaires are in constant use irrespective of daylight conditions. Nor is it eco-virtuous to create spaces which need continuously to be flooded with light without reference to where light is actually required and at what level. Research into Sick Building Syndrome has already revealed the significant contribution slapdash lighting design is making towards the unsympathetic effect of working areas flooded with shadowless light of an unsuitable colour and character, and this effect is already being reconsidered in enlightened quarters.

New thinking on the subject of lighting is therefore likely to lead to a decrease in the use of artificial light as a fixed and continuous architectural feature, and an increased emphasis on making light available, under user control, only when required, on the precise place where it is required and in the exact volume required. Ultra-low energy systems are likely to come into wider use for ambient lighting, so that passage through areas is safe, and visual information available where required, but such systems will need to be examined closely to ensure that the materials of which they are made, and the energy and techniques involved, are not in themselves so environmentally objectionable as to outweigh the attraction of their energy-saving attributes in use. Environmentally-unfriendly materials and manufacturing techniques can involve anything from heavy metals to CFCs, and if the high cost to the consumer of some of the latest new-energy systems is any guide, the energy expenditure during manufacture may be high indeed.

LIME

Limestone, the source of lime, has been the basis of various building traditions throughout Britain for centuries, not only in its own right but as the raw material for cement, concrete, plaster, certain types of bricks, and blocks and slabs for a multitude of uses. Lime is used in steel-making, in agriculture, in gardening and horticulture generally, for water treatment and in innumerable industrial processes. It is also a constituent of a host of materials ranging from paints and industrial finishes to the most sophisticated electronic equipment. It is used as roadstone, as railway-line ballast and as a construction industry aggregate. Today it is even used in the process by which the flue gas emissions of power stations are purified to avoid pollution.

It follows that a ban on the use of limestone would completely disrupt building construction as we know it, not to mention all the other industrial processes in which it is used, and therefore such a proposal would be unrealistic. Yet anyone who has observed the consequences of large-scale limestone quarrying and the production of lime and cement in such places as the Peak District National Park in Derbyshire, or in Ribblesdale in the Yorkshire Dales National Park, would agree that the present extent of limestone extraction in Britain alone (it is also highly destructive in other countries) must be questioned. If those planning permissions already granted for the extraction of limestone are fully implemented, entire ranges of hills in areas of outstanding natural beauty will be destroyed within the lifespan of our children. There is growing pressure therefore for the present rate of growth in the use of the stone to be restricted. It has understandably been suggested that if these quarries and the associated lime-kilns were in the Home Counties, the search for alternative materials and technologies would already have been addressed with more urgency.

Green thinking on building design, techniques and materials therefore focuses on finding an alternative to limestone-based products. Research into alternative sources of lime, such as seawater, needs to be intensified, though this will produce the material in powder form only, and thus limits its relevance. In the meantime, the Green attitude is to seek uses of lime which enable the material to be recycled, and which extend the lifespan of the structure created as long as possible. It is therefore highly undesirable environmentally to use limestone-based materials in structures designed to have a short life. Such constructions should be created as far as possible, including interior finishes, from materials from renewable sources.

LIMESTONE

The comments above on lime obviously apply to limestone, but with certain reservations. When the stone is used in a vernacular way, in walls, floors, pavements or roofing, its potential life is almost infinite. If it is quarried in the old way, with small-scale extraction from suitable beds as close to the place of use as possible, its use can be regarded as environment-friendly, although it is of course non-renewable.

Using limestone in such a way, however, calls for close observation of local building and design practice and the decentralisation of supply. The line of limestone deposits in Britain runs diagonally across from the south-west, in Devon and Dorset, through the Malvern Hills and the Cotswolds to Northamptonshire, Cambridgeshire, and north through Derbyshire into the Pennines and the Cleveland Hills. In each of these areas, and of outlying regions to the east, west and north of this main line, very localised ways of employing the stone have developed. These vernacular traditions lie at the heart of the special visual character of the villages and towns which have evolved in them. Sometimes, even within a few miles, the methods of employing stone change completely. A comparison of the sandstone columns in Gloucester Cathedral with the use of the stone in the tiny churches and cottages, barns and farmhouses in the hills to the east of the Cathedral illustrates this point.

It follows that genuinely environment-friendly use of limestone – and, indeed of any indigenous building stone – is not compatible with the usual standardised building practices and product ranges offered in the building industry. The Green policy on the use of stone calls for individual attention to vernacular design detailing and to construction techniques which are indigenous to the area. This approach is completely contrary to the recent trend, which is towards buildings with traditional overtones but which are actually a mixture of quasi-vernacular themes from random areas, and standardised country-wide factory-made components. It does not follow that this trend, in the last resort, is more economical than the Green approach, which relies on materials close to hand.

LINOLEUM            (See Floorings)

## MARBLE

The scale of destruction of the visual environment and the countryside in areas of Italy and Portugal, to mention only two instances, in the quarrying for marble, granite and other building stones is so great as to defy description and render even limestone quarrying in Britain almost innocuous in comparison. If we are to continue to employ such materials as marble for floors and for exterior cladding, therefore, their use must be confined to structures designed for an indefinite lifespan, and all reasonable steps must be taken to avoid premature ageing or degradation. In theory, marble, like other stones, should be easy to recycle, but unfortunately current building demolition practice means that it rarely achieves a useful further life.

Most marbles degrade relatively quickly if exposed to pollution generally and acid rain in particular. Internal surfaces are obviously not affected in the same way, though where floors are concerned there is an argument for using marble chips in composites, such as terrazzo, in order to improve other qualities and to use the raw material more efficiently (see Stone).

## METALS

In a sense there is no such thing as an environmentally-friendly metal, because virtually all metals are derived from raw materials which are obtained destructively, and considerable amounts of energy are used to refine them from these raw materials and transport them to the point of use.

The processing of certain metals uses vast amounts of energy, which are currently not recycled where this would be possible at the end of the process. Therefore most metals are not only non-renewable, but energy-expensive in addition.

### Ferrous

The iron and steel industry is the biggest user of energy among the high industrial consumers, and also the largest generator of clean waste heat, which could be recovered through the installation of the appropriate equipment. Iron casting also produces concentrated heat loss from the top of the iron-melting cupolas. This waste gas has a high calorific value but is contaminated, and produced only intermittently.

The iron castings industry consumes some 22 PJ of energy. Of this, 45 per cent is from coke; 25 per cent natural gas; 18 per cent electricity and 12 per cent oil.

PJ stands for petajoule. One PJ equals 10 to the 15 joules, a joule being a basic energy unit (1 KwH = 3,600,000 J = 3.6 MJ). Thus PJ are large energy units suitable for expressing energy consumption a million times greater than the amounts which are normally of interest to heating engineers.

### Non-Ferrous

Aluminium and Copper are in the Energy Efficiency Office's list of High-Temperature Process Industries. In the non-ferrous industries aluminium uses 78 PJ, of which 60 per cent is used in the reduction of the metal from the oxide. About 2 PJ is wasted in the melting and holding of the metal and while gases are contaminated during fluxing for about 5 per cent of the cycle, particulate levels at other times are low. The industry has generally been slow to incorporate heat recovery technology as a means of improving energy efficiencies. The total energy consumption of the copper industry in the survey year (1982) was 10 PJ, of which about a quarter was lost as waste gases from refining and remelting furnaces. Clean gases are generated in reheating and heat treatment furnaces. Little attempt has been made to recover this heat.

It is true that most metals can be recycled, and such recycling is now an essential element of the steelmaking process in Britain. However, while it is easy to recycle items made of single materials it can be all but impossible to do so with an item composed of dissimilar substances.

In each of the countries mentioned below, the mining and quarrying activity used to obtain the raw material is causing environmental destruction on a massive scale, both directly and indirectly.

### Aluminium

The most abundant metal on the Earth's crust. Refining it from bauxite is a very high-energy process. Tiny amounts of aluminium occur naturally in the bodies of mammals, but in large amounts it can cause a variety of health risks. One such arises out of aluminium as a contaminant of drinking water.

### Cadmium

Mainly obtained as a by-product of the refining of zinc, copper and lead, though it occurs naturally as the mineral greenockite. Cadmium compounds are poisonous, and its manufacture involves considerable pollution risks.

### Chromium

Mined mainly as chromite in the Soviet Union and Zimbabwe. Used for plating, which produces many highly toxic waste products. It is used in the dye industry as a pigment and is a component in certain special steels.

### Copper

Mined mainly in the form of the sulphide chalcopyrite or the carbonate malachite in Zambia, Zaire, Chile, Australia and New Guinea.

### Lead

Soluble compounds of lead are toxic and, like most heavy metals, accumulative in the body. Lead paintwork applied more than 20 years ago may contain considerable amounts of lead, and should not be burned off or stripped by a dry method, which causes dust, but by some moist form which contains the old paint. The debris from stripped lead paint must be regarded as toxic waste for disposal purposes.

In obtaining all these metals, roads are built and industrial buildings erected which deface the landscape. Many of the processes involved cause pollution on a massive scale, with liquid effluents and sludge poisoning rivers and the sea, and releasing huge quantities of toxic gases which pollute the atmosphere. Secondary processes, such as plating, are also high on the list of ecosinful industrial activity. They create toxic by-products and wastes which inevitably re-enter the environment as pollutants of the atmosphere, land or water eventually. When these factors are taken into consideration, any view that metals are environmentally preferable to plastics has to be reconsidered, especially in building applications, and the search for alternative materials from relatively benign sources accelerated.

Once we have accepted that the extraction and production of metals is environmentally highly destructive, much can be done to reduce their environmental impact. In their manufacture, secondary uses can be devised for the vast amounts of heat which are at present wasted, and neighbouring industrial use made of such heat and of other wastes wherever possible. Slag as a waste of smelting processes is already being exploited, to some extent, in this way.

METHANE

A gas arising from the decomposition of organic matter. Like butane and propane, it occurs naturally in oil wells, though to a lesser extent. It is also produced in marshes, and arises from human communities in sewage, slurry and organic waste in landfill site (see Waste). It could then be used positively for heating, but is mostly burnt off wastefully, because otherwise it is dangerously explosive. It is thus clear that ecologically-minded designers can devise positive uses for methane, especially when it arises from domestic sewage.

Methane is causing increasing concern among environmental scientists because of its ability to lock heat from the sun into the atmosphere, contributing to the global warming which now threatens the planet. Early in 1989, in evidence submitted to the House of Commons Energy Select Committee, Open University scientists warned that it has become urgently necessary that methane in existing landfill sites be gathered and burnt off. The University proposed a national network of rubbish incinerators, feeding the heat to district heating schemes. This could, they reported, save 6 million tonnes of coal and 12 to 16 million tonnes of carbon dioxide.

MICA                    A non-renewable mineral; any of a group of hydrous potassium aluminium silicates, useful because it is layered. Micas containing very little iron are used as thermal or electrical insulators, and ground mica is used in wallpapers, roofing paper, paint, and as a filler, a lubricant, an absorbent and a packing material. So far, no renewable substitute has been found, and its extraction is destructive to the environment (see also Vermiculite).

MICROWAVE               (See Kitchen Design)

MOSAIC                  (See Floorings)

NITRATES          (See Water)

NOBLE GASES       So called because they have no tendency to mix with other gases. They are Argon, Helium, Krypton, Neon, Radon and Xenon. Apart from Radon, the only one of concern in the present context, they can all be obtained from the atmosphere. Radon, the heaviest, is colourless and formed in the earth from the radioactive decay of uranium. Traces of it exist everywhere at ground level, but it is found most abundantly above rock formations such as granite. It therefore collects in houses on these formations, and as a result, particular attention is paid to achieving good ventilation in these dwellings. Examples are buildings in Cornwall. The fact that natural radiation of this kind exists is sometimes used to blur the argument against man-made radiation sources.

Dr C. Samuelsson of the University of Lund in Sweden has developed a method of retrospective estimation of exposure to radon in buildings through measuring the isotopes of polonium on window panes and picture glass (see Appendix).

NOISE             A major pollutant in modern society.
Internal noise in dwellings can be controlled by seeing that soil stacks and water services are not near sensitive areas, such as bedrooms and living-rooms; that the access panels to services are not in sensitive rooms and, in the case of apartments, by ensuring that the rooms of adjacent buildings are compatible. Floors should have airborne-sound insulation built in. Carpets and underlays on

floors and stairs should reduce impact noise, and the door to any under-stair cupboard should be solid core and well-fitted. Care should be taken to avoid direct air paths caused by holes or gaps. Stud partitions should be noise-insulated with a 25 mm absorbent quilt in the cavity. Buffer zones should be created between dwellings such as terraced houses. Further reduction in sound convection can be achieved through the use of chipboard in which the chips are bound by cement rather than resin (see Boards; Solvents). Cement-bonded chipboard is slow to combust and insect-resistant.

In steel- and timber-framed dwellings and all-timber houses, which incorporate fewer environmentally-destructive materials than conventional housing, the design of separating walls is important, and the thickness of the quilting may need to be increased. Long nails through the 'floating floors' to the joists should be avoided.

*External* sources of noise, such as road traffic, railways, air traffic and industries nearby, can be dealt with by: screening with trees and shrubs along the site boundaries, grassland rather than hard surfaces outside where possible; secondary glazing of windows with glass not less than 6 mm thick; the installation of ventilators instead of windows to admit fresh air on the noisy side; improved roof insulation; improved insulation of separating walls. In concrete constructions cracks and gaps can be made good in the concrete, and mineral fibre quilting and cellular plasterboard on the walls, with similar quilting between the concrete and the 'floating' floor (see Appendix).

Although the use of flammable polyurethane foam in furniture became illegal, because of its liability to cause fires, on 1 November 1988 (see Rubber), it is still legal to use it in sound-proofing. However, fibreglass, which is inflammable, is to be preferred (see also Insulation).

NYLON                    (See Plastics; Fibres; Textiles)

OILS

**Fatty**

Mixtures of glycerides of fatty acids from animals and plants such as tung, linseed, rape, coconut, palm and so on.

**Mineral**

Mixtures of hydrocarbons from petroleum, shale or coal.

Crude oil is a fundamentally valuable non-renewable natural resource which should be treated as precious environmental capital, used as a petrochemical feedstock, for specialised pharmaceutical and other industrial uses where it is so far irreplaceable, or for the manufacture of products which can be recycled or have an indefinite life in the environment. Plastics, for example, if their production and use is within an environmental framework, are environment-friendly (see Plastics). To squander crude oil as fuel, when its potential energy is being utilised at relatively low efficiencies, and when it produces major pollutants, is ecologically criminal. If we continue to burn oil mainly in power stations and car engines, this marvellous resource will be exhausted in commercial quantities within a few decades, leaving our descendants to wrestle with the consequential damage to the world climate as well as a host of other pollution problems. If we switched to using renewable sources, such as hydrocarbons from sea-water and farmed vegetable oils, for fuel and other bulk applications, the use of crude oil as a resource for selective uses could continue for centuries.

**Essential**

Ethereal oils contained in some plants which give flowers their characteristic odour. Many belong to the terpene group, others relate to benzene.

An EC Directive on Waste Oil will shortly become effective. It will deal with the registration of waste-oil collectors, the licensing of processors and the imposition of emission limits in certain categories of oils.

Much waste oil is purified, distilled or 'laundered' for re-use. It should never be discharged down household drains, where it causes major problems (see Sewage).

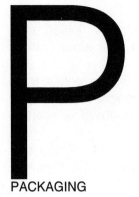

PACKAGING

Materials for packaging can be *Metal*, *Glass*, for which bottle banks are available; *Plastics*, and *Paper and Board*. In this last category packaging uses 85 per cent of all paper and board manufactured in the UK and is the most desirable environmentally as paper and cardboard can be recycled indefinitely.

Packaging is useful in preserving goods, and therefore has environmental advantages, but its nature is important. Non-renewable materials are environmentally-undesirable, as are those which combine more than one type of material, such as composites of aluminium and cardboard. These are impossible to recycle and should not be used. A newly-recognised hazard is the use of CFCs in expanded-foam packaging for fast-food outlets. This should be banned as quickly as possible, and consumers should avoid retailers who pack food in this type of container.

It is now possible to obtain almost all grades of rigid and flexible plastic packaging foams from makers who do not use CFCs. However, non-plastic alternatives should be sought, because currently there is no environmentally-friendly method available for the disposal of plastic waste. To bury it in landfill sites is merely to store up problems for future generations. To incinerate it, which is a good way to recover the energy contained, necessitates expensive equipment and control, otherwise ecologically-damaging toxic flue gases are released. Ideally, recyclable plastics should be available for these uses, along with the necessary facilities for the recycling process at the disposal point. Paper packaging can in theory be recycled, so can the one-polymer plastic PET, (see Plastics) but again we await the necessary facilities, both in the domestic and in the industrial sphere. It is true that much industrial paper and board packaging is now recycled, but similar facilities for plastics are practically non-existent in the UK.

Environmentalists would like to see a low-tech approach to packaging. This would undoubtedly mean a greater use of re-cycled paper. Offices dispose of tons of paper and board waste, and there should be immediate pressure for all such establishments to recycle this automatically. There remains the type of waste paper which cannot be recycled because it is contaminated with non-paper material, such as shiny magazine paper or paper combined with metal, plastic coating or special printing inks. This material is eminently suitable for shredding and using for packaging material, after which it can be disposed of by burning, which can be done quite satisfactorily with minimum pollution risk.

Flammable polyurethane foam, illegal in furniture, may still be used in packaging. It is, of course, non-renewable and environmentally undesirable.

PAINT

Most paints incorporate solvents, or dyestuffs and other materials from petrochemical sources (see Solvents). Such paints, and related surface finishes such as epoxy lacquers and polyurethane varnishes, are widely and casually used in the building industry, as well as domestically, without any thought for environmental or health consequences. The death of a young paint-worker in 1989 from leukemia has increased concern about carcinogenic chemicals in paint. Research is urgently necessary into this whole question.

Many of the materials used in paint application would in a manufacturing context involve strict control of ventilation, extraction of toxic fumes, protective clothing and breathing apparatus. Yet the domestic user and many builders are appallingly casual in handling these paints and finishes.

Some manufacturers are now developing paints based on vegetable oils, or are relying on emulsion techniques which do not involve the release of toxic vapour during drying. Others are re-examining the use of natural dyestuffs based on different types of earth and vegetable materials (see Pigments and Dyes). However, certain colours, mainly those deriving from metals such as lead, tin, titanium, chromium, mercury and cadmium, can at present only be obtained by processes which create toxic wastes. These are produced either when the base material is first refined or during the manufacture of the paint. Most of them cause harmful effluents during manufacture and are cumulative poisons within the body. As the scene is changing rapidly now that these facts are increasingly being recognised, it is best that consumers should enquire, when purchasing paints or painted finishes, about the type of dyes used and the dangers of application (see also Finishes)

PANELS            (See Boards)

PAPER             This is an ambivalent material from the Green point of view. While it is largely made from softwoods, and can be recycled, its manufacture has resulted in the development of vast conifer forests which are ecologically almost deserts, in which few habitats can survive. They also cause soil erosion, and heighten the acidity of lakes and rivers. Ninety million trees are felled each year to supply Britain's demand for paper and board. Moreover, during manufacture large amounts of energy are used, vast quantities of water are extracted and a huge volume of pollutant waste is produced, usually including dioxins as a by-product of chlorine-based bleaches, all so that we can have brilliant white tissues and the like.

In the production of white paper and paper-pulp products, such as babies' nappies and tampons, chlorine bleaches are used which not only pollute the outflows of water into rivers, but can render the product dangerous (see Appendix). But unbleached, cream-coloured tampons and nappies are now becoming available. New bleaching techniques, based on oxygen rather than chlorine, will reduce the toxic waste problem to some degree, but we must learn that it is pointless to strive for pure white paper in uses in which it is quite unnecessary: internal office memos, toilet paper, packaging, and envelopes, for example, could all be cream or coloured. Recycled paper is no longer a dreary grey. The manufacturing processes would thus be simplified and the products might even become cheaper.

Quite a reasonable case could be made for plastic bags as a Green alternative to paper for shoppers, even if shopping bags are made from recycled paper, because paper is not a low-energy material. Best of all is to use a shopping basket, of course.

More than 89 per cent of the paper pulp used in Britain is imported: in 1987 imports amounted to 1,682,000 tonnes, in addition to 5,282,500 tonnes of paper and board, of which we consumed 8,700,000 tonnes. If we made our own pulp from recycling paper this would reduce imports, lessen pollution and save up to 50 per cent energy. Moreover, the Department of the Environment saves around £4000 a year by incorporating recycled paper into its stationery consumption. If all large paper users followed suit, and if we had a national framework for recycling paper throughout Britain, the energy savings which resulted could bring the price down sufficiently for us to subsist on home-produced paper, reducing imports and creating employment: there is great potential for jobs in the paper-recycling industry. The Netherlands have shown the way by stabilising supply; their largest wastepaper-consuming mills have made a cooperating agreement with the wastepaper trade, and an independent company has been set up which is empowered to buy buffer stocks at times of excess supply and low prices, and release them at times of shortage and high prices.

The environmental advantages of the use of paper would be enhanced tremendously if it only came from sustainable, mixed forestry; if its manufacture were to be subject to strict environmental control; if no chlorine bleaches were used; if recycling or shredding (see Packaging) facilities became universal, and if we followed the Dutch marketing and supply techniques (see also Waste).

PARTICLE BOARDS    (See Boards)

PESTICIDES    The rapidly increasing effect of the manufacture and use of pesticides on all aspects of life on this planet renders them of fundamental importance to environmentalists. Every time a person feels the need to use a pesticide the need itself should be queried, and if one must be used it should be selected with the greatest care.

Recent improvements in analytical techniques have drawn attention to hitherto unsuspected levels of pesticide contamination of drinking water. The EC directive enshrined in British legislation concerning water imposes a limit of five parts per million for total pesticide contamination in tap water. At the time this was first proposed this represented an effective zero. However, a combination of different pesticides now accumulating in underground aquifers, and our developing ability to detect substances in increasingly-minute concentrations, mean that we now know that this limit is being exceeded in many parts of Britain. The situation has been confused by a second set of guidelines from the Department of the Environment concerning maximum contamination levels which have now been issued to the water industry. These tacitly sanction much higher levels of contamination by some forty of the more common pesticides. Many of those currently causing the greatest problems are substances used in industry, building, construction and the public utilities, but not in agriculture or horticulture.

The widely-held assumption that the agrarian use of herbicides, fungicides and suchlike are responsible for the worst pollutants from pesticides is not justified by the facts. We now know that industry and the public utilities are increasingly to blame.

There are two reasons why the non-agricultural use of pesticides contributes disproportionately to water contamination. The first is that the newer biodegradable formulations of many pesticides depend on the substance falling on, or passing into soil for the process to be effective. But if it is sprayed, for example, onto gravel or ballast draining into a watercourse or aquifer it may be washed straight through without touching soil. Once this occurs little or no biodegradation takes place, and the substance is merely diluted. It can thus pass through sewage sludge or irrigation into drinking water and food.

The second reason is that controls of usage, application and disposal of waste are not exercised so effectively on non-agricultural activities. Leakage from storage tanks, lax observance of manufacturers' instructions on strength, applications and precautions relating to weather, not to mention thoughtless washing into storm drains, contribute steadily to the build-up of pollution.

There are still a number of very eco-unfriendly pesticides, such as Aldrin, which, although no longer manufactured, remain on the shelf or in the garden shed. The building industry in particular still retains stocks of such undesirables, which should be sought out and handed in to police stations or other authorities for destruction.

Aldrin has been widely blamed for the crash in the number of falcons, otters and other predators in Britain in the 1960s. Although no longer manufactured for agricultural use, it is still present in the formulae for timber treatment.

As yet no alternative methods or materials have been devised for the use of pesticides in various applications, such as an eco-friendly wood preservative or fungicide. It is true that there are substances recommended for treating timbers which are less harmful to bats, but other wild species are also threatened by toxic organic substances, and so are human beings. It is to be hoped that more resources will be devoted to the search for safer methods. Meanwhile existing pesticides should be used sparingly and under strict control.

PIGMENTS AND DYES

**Natural**
Few of the traditional dyes, such as cochineal, golden rod, ling, logwood tree, onion skins and walnut juice, are now used industrially, though some craft workers still make use of them. A small number of dyestuffs and pigments are still obtained from cochineal, but the vast majority are based on synthetic compounds.

**Man-made**

These are mostly derived from benzene, toluene, xylenes, naphthalene, anthracene, and the phenols. None of these is renewable, all being obtained either from the distillation of coal tar or more recently, and increasingly, from petroleum. The dyestuffs industry is highly technological, and produces dangerous effluent which is seriously affecting British rivers.

PLASTER    (See Finishes)

PLASTICS    Can be defined as substances composed of a mixture of organic materials. Nature produces its own plastics: peat and pitch for example. Plastics can be created from any biomass, but at the moment, apart from a few raw materials such as milk casein (buttons, etc.), wood and cotton (celluloid, textiles and paints), and rubber latex (vulcanised articles), most are made from oil, natural gas, coal and salt. Ten out of every hundred litres of refined oil are currently used in plastics manufacture. Theoretically, the use of plastics is to a certain extent environmentally benign, because plastic articles, such as the ubiquitous plastic bag, can be re-used many times, and in theory they can be recycled. But in practice the matter is more complicated. Briefly, if recycling facilities were provided for recyclable plastic articles, and collection and incinerators made available for the rest, plastics could become renewable or otherwise environmentally benign. As things are at present, they are not.

Plastics fall into three categories: *Thermoplastics*, which soften when heated; *Hard Plastics*, which are resistant to high temperatures; *Elastomers*, such as foams, which are rubbery.

All can be burned in incineration plants of sufficiently high temperatures, and thus produce energy for heating. In the case of polyvinyl chloride (PVC) plastic, 'scrubbers' are needed after incineration to avoid the emission of chlorine into the atmosphere.

The best plastics from the environmental point of view are those which can be recycled. One example is the rigid material used in milk crates; in Germany all of these are automatically recycled, the ideal situation. Another is the increasing use of polyethylene terephthalate (PET) in place of PVC. PET is composed of only one polymer, and this simplicity of structure enables it to be recycled endlessly. More and more manufacturers are changing from the use of PVC to PET for their containers. Moreover, the production of PET bottles uses only 60 per cent of the energy used to make glass bottles and only 25 per cent of that used to make aluminium cans. But in the UK at the time of writing there are few facilities for recycling PET.

As yet there is no means of identifying plastics made from the one-polymer, recyclable plastic PET. The reason given for this by the manufacturers is that it is pointless until there is a collection system which will deliver the PET to a recycling facility. In the USA a recyclable symbol – a triangle of arrows – is being incorporated in shampoo bottle moulds made from PVC. The material is then reprocessed and used for pipes, extruded sheeting and bottles.

A problem in the domestic use of plastics is that they are not biodegradable (do not rot down when discarded). Research is in progress on the development of a plastic, for bags, which will rot down in the environment. The material is derived from sugar by a natural bacterial process, and positive results are being obtained, but it will be some time before mass production can start (see Appendix). Until this is developed, recycling remains the most desirable solution to the problem of plastics disposal, and energy-producing incineration the second-best.

Plastics are already made on occasions from renewable sources, and this trend is increasing.

There is no reason other than availability and relatively low cost why oil has to be the main raw material from which plastics are made. In fact, certain types of plastic materials of importance to the building industry are already based on organic and thus renewable sources. These include formaldehyde, from slaughterhouse waste; casein from milk, and cellulose from wood, in addition to a large number of resins and gums, as well as rubber latex. Materials based on pitch or bitumen from asphalt lakes, rather than refined crude oil, may also be regarded as a benign exploitation of a natural, self-renewing resource. As the cost of oil as a hydrocarbon raw material increases, and its availability reduces, alternatives will increasingly be sought. These are likely to range from processed plant material and oilseeds to hydrocarbons extracted from sea-water. Until that time arrives, Green efforts will be directed towards confining the use of oil-derived plastics to applications in which they are environmentally the lesser evil. In many building applications, plastics offer a low-energy, long-lasting, lightweight alternative to traditional materials, and are thus ecologically preferable to some evanescent materials even though they may be less visually attractive.

It is difficult to recycle composite materials and constructions, such as glass-reinforced plastics (GRP) and plastic-covered cables, except by incineration at high temperatures and heat-recovery for further use.

Green designers are therefore endeavouring to use single plastics in pure form, labelling them clearly, so that non-destructive recycling is possible. For the same reason, designers should balance the advantages of using plastics in coating, bonding and sealing applications against the risk that this may preclude future recycling (see also Foam; Rubber).

## PLUMBING

The privatisation of water supplies in the UK, and the dropping of trade barriers in 1992, are likely to have a fundamental effect upon plumbing in this country. Designers and consumers should be aware of the likely changes, and should press their Euro and national MPs to follow the Green policies.

It is not generally realised that a number of modern WC cisterns are dual-flush, a facility which is provided by making a hole in precisely the right place in the syphon. A short flush is then obtained by depressing and immediately releasing the lever, whereas a long flush is obtained by holding the lever down until the tank is empty. Unfortunately plumbers often place a rubber bung in this hole at installation, thus removing the dual-flush facility. Many owners of modern WCs will therefore discover on examining their cistern that they can achieve the facility by simply removing this little bung.

Dual-flush cisterns are a Green step forward, and it is most

unfortunate that in 1992 it is envisaged that Britain will change from
dual-flush to the continental practice of using 7.5-litre cisterns. It is
calculated in the trade that the average person uses the loo twenty
times a day, requiring a short flush of the cistern, which is 4.5 litres,
on seventeen of these visits. It takes little calculation to show that
seventeen flushes of a 7.5-litre tank uses over 162 litres of expensive
water, whereas seventeen short flushes of a dual-flush tank uses only
76 litres. Over the whole of Britain, this change in 1992 would
therefore mean wasting millions of litres of water. Not only would this
be environmentally damaging; it would also mean heavier bills for the
consumer if water meters are installed in every house, as is currently
the intention.

The changes in 1992 will also result in an increase in imports of
plumbing fittings, and the existing water byelaws will be replaced by
the new water regulations, which will certainly mean changes in
plumbing methods. An indication of these is the recent legislation on
pressurised water systems. The traditional British low-pressure
plumbing system, based on the use of an open loft tank or the Fortic-
type alternative, demands a lower degree of skill and good practice
than the high-pressure continental alternative. Consequently, casual
DIY or unskilled trade attempts to modify or service high-pressure
installations could become disastrous. Nevertheless the cost
advantages of installing mains pressurised systems will certainly lead
to their widespread adoption, both for new constructions and for major
renovations.


British-manufactured kitchen sink mixer taps provide for complete
separation of the hot and the cold supply. In part this protects the
mains from feed-back contamination, but it also ensures that there
is no risk of contaminating cold drinking water from the mains with
hot water which lost its chlorine safety protection in the loft tank,
with the resulting possibility of a massive increase in bacterial
population. Continental taps, which mix hot and cold within the
system can therefore, when run on British low-pressure systems,
supply at least a glass-full of potentially contaminated water before
the tap is flushed out with safe water from the mains. So far no

serious attempt has been made to enforce byelaws which could prevent the use of such taps in British kitchens, but such an attempt may well become necessary in the future.

PLYWOOD                (See Wood)

POLLUTION              (See Acid Rain; Noise; Paper; Waste.)

POLYESTER              (See Finishes; Plastics; Textiles)

POLYPROPYLENE          (See Plastics)

POLYSTYRENE            (See Plastics)

POLYURETHANE           (See Plastics)

PONDS                  In these days when British wetlands are disappearing almost daily, the provision of a pond in a garden is most helpful to the environment. Most valuable of all are ponds with no fish added; merely oxygenated plants. This enables a rich growth of flora and fauna, including frogs, toads and newts, which will gradually develop without any further action. Goldfish are more useful when a couple are popped into rainwater barrels to eat mosquito and other larvae. Ice in winter should be pierced for aeration by the use of floating objects or holes made with hot saucepan bases.

PRESERVATIVES          It is obviously necessary to seek to preserve the soundness of timber in building applications. However, many highly toxic substances which have been banned for agricultural purposes for years are still in common use in the building industry as preservative insecticides and fungicides, or for the treatment of pest infestations. Apart from the direct health risk to operatives during application, and subsequently to those occupying the building, this situation prolongs environmental damage by many unpleasant, persistent and – in the case of organochlorines – extremely dangerous substances.

It is possible to treat softwoods to give them a life expectancy equal to that of alternative hardwoods, but great care must be taken to ensure that this is done without danger to those involved in the treatment, to those potentially exposed to fumes and runoff, and those carrying out subsequent work. Meanwhile, research is urgently needed to discover preservatives which are genuinely safe in application to softwoods in building construction (see Trace Organics; Timber Treatment)

PRESSURE
COOKERS

(See Domestic Kitchen)

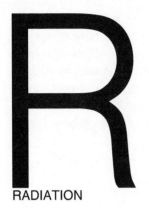

# R

RADIATION

This is a rapidly-developing environmental hazard, still not properly understood and largely unrecognised in legislation. It threatens under various headings.

Radioactive emissions from nuclear power stations and from nuclear decay in the waste from those stations, as well as from other waste, such as from hospital X-ray equipment, are recognised as being dangerous, but we still do not know enough about their effects.

Evidence has recently come to light concerning the possible danger to people who live near electric power cables from the electro-magnetic radiation coming from these. The subject is under investigation, but the creation of new building estates or commercial enterprises near overhead electricity cables would seem to be undesirable until more is know of the potential hazard.

Another recent development is the recognition that the visual display units (VDUs) of computers can have a deleterious effect on operators who spend hours watching these every day, especially pregnant women. Eyes are also affected.

A survey carried out by the Canadian Labour Congress showed that VDU workers experienced eye and vision problems twice as often as non-VDU workers. This is not actually caused by radiation, but by eye-muscle fatigue, inadequate lighting, screen flickers and the build-up of static electricity on the screens. It is recommended that workers should not spend more than four hours a day at the screens, with fifteen-minute breaks every hour.

Some employers provide special smocks which they claim reduce the risk of radiation hazards, but the metallised fabric used cannot block ionising radiation, and is flammable, emitting fumes when it is burned which may be toxic.

Food irradiation is purely a device for increasing profits by extending the shelf-life of foodstuffs, especially fresh fruit. Commercial interests have long exerted pressure to legalise its use in Britain, and they were finally successful in June 1989, when the Government announced its intention to do so. It is important that all irradiated food should be labelled as such, so that the consumer can exercise intelligent choice when buying fresh foods.

It is known that the type of radiation used does not render the food radioactive, but there are other hazards. The process creates chemical substances known as radiolytic products, and the effect of some of these on the human body is as yet untested. Irradiation also results in loss of vitamin content, especially in fresh fruit and vegetables. Moreover, cases have been known of foodstuffs being condemned on arrival in British ports as not fresh, and then returned to the port of issue, irradiated to mask the stale appearance, and accepted on return (see Energy; Noble Gases).

RADON      (See Noble Gases)

ROOFING      (See material concerned and Vernacular Design)

RUBBER

**Natural**
The process of extracting rubber latex from trees is renewable, and its use is the more environmentally-desirable now that exhausted rubber-wood can be used as a renewable timber resource. However, natural rubber cannot be used in all applications; some, such as seals in oil and gas processing, need synthetic rubber.

**Synthetic**
This is non-renewable, being a product of the petroleum industry, and thus environmentally undesirable, It should therefore only be used in applications for which natural rubber is unsuitable.

**Foam**
From 1 November 1988 the manufacturers of foam-filled furniture have been obliged to use 'combustion-modified foam', this being less flammable than polyurethane foam. From 1 March 1989 all furniture from first-hand retail outlets has had to use the safer foam. From 1 March 1990 the outer covers of furniture will have to pass the lighted match test, garden furniture requirements will be changed to come into line, along with built-in furniture in caravans, and the Furniture Safety Regulations of 1980 will be completely revoked. Second-hand furniture sales come under the provisions of the new regulations on 1 March 1993.

**Recycling**
Both natural and synthetic rubber will degrade by oxidative processes in the environment. Moreover, both can be broken down and reclaimed for low-specification products. More facilities should be provided for recycling rubber.

RUBBISH                    (See Waste)

# S

SAFETY

The tradition of the building industry concerning the safety of operatives is appalling. Major companies, it is true, through pressure from Health and Safety at Work legislation, and some massive compensation awards, are gradually taking a more responsible attitude, but contracts for 'small works' and minor building projects are not. In fact, they are probably becoming more irresponsible.

Small building projects often involve a shifting population of subcontract labour and self-employed craft workers. On such sites there is usually the traditional attitude of regarding safety precautions with a mixture of ignorance and macho stupidity. At the same time potential hazards from new materials and technologies are increasing steadily. There are inspectors who travel round looking at such sites, but they are very thin on the ground, so that regular monitoring is impossible.

Greens would like to see stricter application of the Health and Safety at Work legislation, which really means making enough money available to provide sufficient inspectors for regular monitoring of small building sites. Meanwhile, specifiers and site owners can make a direct contribution to encouraging safety-consciousness by including comprehensive safety-related clauses in all works specifications and schedules for quotation, to ensure that there is no direct financial incentive to ignore safety and thus cut costs. Greens hope that in time this will become a legal as well as a moral obligation.

SAND and GRAVEL    (See Aggregates)

SANITARY WARE    This is an area in which built-in obsolescence has almost taken over. There is now no British manufacturer of cast-iron baths, the life-span of which is almost indefinite, as they can be re-enamelled when necessary. Most of the new alternative materials in use have a predictable, limited life, and usually cannot be recycled, as they are frequently made from composite materials. The environmentally-conscious consumer therefore scours builders' dumps for re-usable ceramic fittings and old cast-iron baths. Also, Green consumers specify dual-flush WC cisterns, which save a considerable amount of water (see Plumbing).

SEALANTS    These frequently have a limited service life before they degrade, either through natural chemical processes or because of weathering. Thus a sealant may limit the potential lifespan of the structure on which it has been used. Most manufacturers of sealants can provide comprehensive information on the likely performance of their products, and Green designers should investigate this before specifying the product. Sometimes traditional mechanical methods of weatherproofing and draught prevention, or vernacular 'old-fashioned' methods of cladding and sealing joints are preferable to the use of sealants.

Modern building techniques rely heavily on a host of sealants to simplify building processes and cut specialist labour costs. They are also frequently used to facilitate the use of structural materials which could not be employed otherwise. In a few cases, such as flexible joints between concrete components, sealants are actually a long-term improvement on the traditional alternative. But as the Green policy is to cut out as much use of habitat-destructive cement and aggregates as possible, and return to vernacular, renewable materials, or the adaptation of existing structures, it is expected that the use of high-tech sealants will decrease.

SEWAGE    The major environmental factor concerning sewage is that contemporary disposal methods discard a major source of nutrients and other products of the earth.

Until the Victorians invented water closets, the 'night soil' from towns was taken to the outlying vegetable gardens and used in the compost. Some modern sewage plants do use a certain amount of their products for fertiliser, but a great deal more needs to be done before we use sewage as sensibly as in the past. In addition, a great deal of money has to be spent by water authorities in removing from our sewage the harmful pollutants which occur in many household cleaners and disinfectants.

Bleach kills the helpful bacteria in septic tanks, so that they become smelly. Disinfectants likewise affect their activity. Water-softening phosphates in detergents have been cut down, but are still undesirable, as they over-enrich rivers and streams, causing the growth of stifling algae. Pure soap is harmless, but of course it creates scum and felting of wool in hard water areas, where probably a biodegradable detergent is most effective. A major source of pollution in sewage is caused by grease and frying oil (which finally emerges as grease) discharged from mass-catering establishments and domestic dwellings.

The grease accumulates in pumping stations and hampers operations, entailing high maintenance costs in clearing it away. Interestingly, the introduction of micro-wave cooking in catering premises has drastically reduced the problem in those premises. Frying oil is one of the worst offenders, and should be disposed of at source when it is renewed, not poured down the drains. If it is mixed with solid kitchen waste, including uneaten food, it can be used for composting or pigswill.

Cost-effective and highly-automated small-scale sewage treatment processes have now been developed (see Appendix). They range from a glass-reinforced plastic system with a tiny 1 cubic-metre mesophilic anaerobic digester, which will serve a group as small as fifteen people, to packaged sludge digestion plants which can be duplicated to serve large populations, and are already being used by some water authorities.

If resources were made available to exploit these and other techniques we could clean up Britain's beaches and the farm slurry polluting our rivers (see also Sanitary Ware; Waste).

SLAG

Various forms of slag are now reprocessed into useful building materials, in the manner of foamed slag, one of the most widely used lightweight aggregates. Greens hope that an increasing number of waste materials will be recycled in this way instead of forming unsightly heaps scarring the countryside.

SLATE

This is one of the most durable of building materials, used currently for external wall cladding, paving, flooring, roofing and damp-proof coursing. It can be obtained with riven textures, can be silky and smooth or rough, sawn, sanded or finely rubbed. Being very hard and denser than granite, it takes a good polish but does not retain it well. Slate is non-renewable but recyclable.

When carved, the texture of the chiselled surfaces contrast well with highly polished parts, and this difference in tone has been exploited by sculptors. North Wales is the chief source of slate, producing blues, purples, blue-grey and variously green slates. From Cornwall, the material is grey and grey-green, with a characteristic lustre. Occasionally naturally-stained red slates become available. Westmorland slate is generally green, and that from North Lancashire is dark blue.

SLOW COOKING

This is a completely different technique from currently-accepted cooking practices, and is extremely energy-efficient. Probably it is the Green cookery method of the future.

In the days when few houses had ovens, most domestic cooking took place over or around the open hearth, but village bakers were already employing slow-cooking techniques, and offered their ovens as a service to their customers after the day's baking was over. The huge brick or clay lined ovens in which bread was baked, in fact, were employed for a number of functions. They worked on the principle of heat conservation somewhat like today's Aga and Rayburn ovens. First they were heated up, often by lighting a fire within the oven itself, and then the resultant conserved heat was used during the slow cooking period; first for bread, then for roasts and pies, and finally for the long, slow cooking of casseroles and stews. Customers would come for their bread and bring various items to be left with the baker for cooling and collection later, so no valuable heat was wasted.

Within the home the only form of slow cooking was stewing in a large iron pot over the fire. As that fire had to be kept going more or less from October until April ended, this was yet another way to make use of waste heat before it disappeared up the roof-hole. Much later, when small iron domestic ranges appeared, it became commonplace to casserole in one of the range ovens. In early ranges this was the best use, because roasting was still done on a spit or within a Dutch oven, rather like half an oil drum set in front of the open hearth. But the high temperatures needed for bread baking could not be reached in the first ranges, hence the production of oatcakes and suchlike on griddles.

Today's kitchens offer few opportunities for using residual heat. Modern stoves do not store it as the old bread ovens did, and uncontrolled heat conservation poses some dangers. Most modern cooking processes utilise a temperature range from 500°F (260°C) down to 275°F (140°C). As water boils at about 100°C, cooking cannot really be said to be taking place at lower temperatures than this. But slow cooking employs temperatures around 105°C. Cooking at this temperature for six to ten hours will tenderise cheaper cuts of meat and create subtle blends of flavours. However, it carries the danger that if the temperature should fall below 90°C there is a risk that bacteria, always present, will be fostered rather than killed. And if it should drift considerably lower you could actually end up eating your last supper. This situation earned the early plug-in electric slow cookers a bad name, and the whole process went out of fashion.

To summarise, though slow cooking is potentially versatile, energy-saving and convenient, the user must be certain that the necessary level of temperature can be maintained. An automatic electric crockpot, such as is produced by Tower, Swan, Pifco and Cordon Bleu, will efficiently provide such safe levels. Their prices are reasonable, between £23 and £33; they take up little space, use about as much energy as a light bulb, and can make delicious meals for many or for just one or two people.

Certain quite sophisticated recipes, too, are actually improved by using slow-cooking methods. A perfect bouillabaise or splendid ragout can be produced, because in such dishes the actual cooking time is not critical. An hour's delay might even improve flavours. For this reason cooker manufacturers are sometimes adding slow-cooking settings to their latest models, and giving details of the technique in their accompanying booklets. Hobs are also being produced which return to a slow simmer after having heated up. All such developments are a welcome move towards economy in the amount of energy consumed in the kitchens.

SOAP                (See Detergents)

SOFTWOODS           (See Wood)

SOLAR HEATING       The sun is the ultimate source of all energy, and increasingly solar panels and solar orientation are being used in architecture. Solar panels are constantly being improved, and it is best to consult an expert for the latest and most economical technique. Houses can now be visited in which most electricity is produced by solar methods (see Appendix).

A new development of interest is Passive Solar Design (PSD). This consists in so aligning houses as to maximise the amount of heat obtained from the sun. Houses built to these principles are south-facing and unshaded, with wide frontages. They have the living areas, glazing and conservatories on their south sides; north-facing windows being smaller and serving rooms less frequently in use. Apart from thus creating cheerful, bright dwellings, if both siting and construction are designed according to PSD principles, over 10 per cent of average annual fuel bills can be saved.

It has been calculated that if PSD principles were adopted, a site density of twenty-four dwellings per hectare could be sustained for detached houses and about thirty dwellings per hectare for mixed development. At higher densities it would become difficult to avoid some houses being seriously obstructed or having poor relative positions. Cost analyses have further shown that the difference between the estimated costs of the original and PSD layouts is well within the margins of uncertainty in cost calculations.

SOLVENTS

The environmental attitude to solvents is determined by the health hazard they represent in their ability to dissolve fats, which of course include body fats, that is, skin grease and the fatty tissue protecting the nerves. The short-term effects arise from single exposures to a large amount of solvent, which can cause dizziness and eventual loss of consciousness; the long-term effects from frequent exposure over many days, which can cause damage to the liver. All solvents can cause dermatitis and nerve disabilities, but each group carries its own hazards.

*Aromatics* are sweet smelling and include toluene, xylene and benzene. Exposure to toluene has been associated with breakdown of genes. It can cause unconsciousness; so can xylene, which is also an irritant. Benzene is both, and also damages the bone-marrow.

*Chlorinated hydrocarbons* smell sickly. They include chloroform, trichloroethylene, carbon tetrachloride, tetrachloroethane, methylene chloride, perchloroethylene, trichloroethane ('Genklene' and 'Clorothene') and trichlorotrifluoroethane ('Arklone'). The first three have been associated with liver damage, and evidence from animal studies of liver cancer. It is possible that this applies to the others, but we do not know.

*Ethers* include diethyl ether, 'Cellusolve', 'THF' and butyl ether. Their smell is familiar to anyone who has entered a hospital. They affect the liver and kidneys, but Cellusolve is less damaging than butyl ether. All produce wheezing, dry coughs and congestion.

*Alcohols* include methanol, ethanol, ethylene glycol, 'IPS' and 'Oxitol'. They affect the liver and kidneys; methanol is especially dangerous, causing blindness and tremors.

*Ketones* include 'Isophorene', 'MEK', 'MIBK' and 'Furfural'. MEK at high levels damages the lungs, followed by coma and death. All have a damaging effect on the liver and kidneys. Some – it is unknown precisely which – can cause paralysis from breakdown of the nerve ends.

Trade names confuse identification; the only way to find out which one you are using is to consult the manufacturers.

The environment is not a bottomless pit which can accept contaminants indefinitely and lose them for all time. Solvents come into the category of trace organics, which will probably become the major pollution issue of the next decade (see Trace Organics). New techniques enable us to trace them in the air we breathe, the water we drink and the food we eat, down to parts-per-trillion. As a result we now know that the earth is becoming a poisonous chemical dump which is undoubtedly contributing to the so-called diseases of civilisation which have appeared relatively recently. So far this pollution has not reached lethal levels, though in certain industries, and in less-developed countries, workers are vulnerable to severe damage.

It is what are known as synergistic interactions, toxic cocktails, which cause Greens the greatest concern. As they break down, solvents and other trace organics interact not only with each other, but also with other substances which possibly occur quite naturally in the environment or our bodies. The resultant effects cannot be scientifically predicted because each example is unique. Moreover, many solvents accumulate in the body, and can lead to long-term health problems which are irreversible, and for which the true cause may never be established.

Green policy is to eliminate the use of all solvents which release vapour into the atmosphere, by developing alternative products and systems. In the meantime everything possible should be done to treat solvents as the toxic substances they really are. This means that all vapours which are produced should be captured at the point of use and disposed of safely.

Solvents are often recovered, distilled and returned to establishments for re-use. Frequently the residues are burned at sea, but this practice is to come under an international ban (see also Adhesives; Finishes; Chemicals).

STEEL                    (See Metals)

STONE                    **General**
Whether Granite, Limestone, Sandstone, Slate, Marble or Quart-

zite, all stone extraction is from quarrying, and therefore is en-vironmentally destructive. But because of its great durability, stone is a Green building material, especially when used in its natural form and in ways which draw upon local design traditions to ensure that the building is protected against premature degradation.

Throughout Britain we can see examples of stone buildings which have lasted for centuries and which, when made of local materials, contribute to the special character of many of our towns and villages. If quarried or mined near to the point of use, stone merges naturally into the existing built environment, and its extraction is relatively unobjectionable when compared, for example, with open-cast mining. Disused stone quarries frequently become sites of special scientific interest. It is only when large-scale quarrying to obtain stone for industrial purposes, such as roadstone, limestone for conversion into lime and cement, or bulk aggregates, that the resulting eyesore disfigures the local environment. However, the use of stone in its natural form in buildings calls for specialised knowledge and skills. Current practice in the industry tends towards eliminating the need for such skills; a tendency which Greens wish to reverse.

In a country which has prided itself on the individuality of regional visual characteristics, stone should have a vital part to play in many areas as a building material. If correctly used, it can provide satisfactory service to generations to come. Greens would like to see an end to its trivialisation and misuse for fireplaces, crazy paving and other unsuitable ornamentation, often miles from its proper context. It must be said, however, that precisely because of its need for craft skills in use stone is expensive. The sympathetic substitution of synthetic stone in areas where stone buildings are part of the local vernacular is often successful, but the material is usually obtained in environmentally-destructive ways. A dilemma of this nature will only be solved when the fundamental organisation of economics has changed so as to encourage crafts and discourage 'cheap' mass-produced materials which contain many hidden ecological costs that the present economic system does not reveal at the point of sale.

The development of the 'glory-hole' method of obtaining crushed rock is an improvement, as it causes little disturbance of wildlife. It entails entering a stone mountain from the top and bringing out the product through a tunnel below. So far it has only been applied to the extraction of granite. Vast resources of crushed rock have been obtained by this method, and are available in most localities, including the south-east of England, as an alternative type of aggregate (see also Granite; Lime; Limestone; Slate).

Synthetic stone is now used in areas such as the Cotswolds because genuine stone is too expensive. But the energy used in making synthetic stone is ecologically a hidden cost; in real values true stone is the economical product.

STOVES, HEATING        (See Heating)

SULPHUR DIOXIDE        (See Acid Rain)

SURFACE FINISHES       (See Finishes)

SYNTHETIC STONE        (See Stone)

# T

TERRAZZO  (See Floorings; Finishes)

TEXTILES  The only renewable, and therefore environmentally-desirable, textiles are the natural fibres: Cotton, Linen, Silk, Wool and the hair and vegetable fabrics.

All man-made textiles are from non-renewable sources, being manufactured from polymers, which are products of the petro-chemical industry. They dry quickly, are less prone to wrinkle, repel dirt and are easy to clean, but they are not absorbent, so that if you perspire while wearing a man-made fabric the moisture runs off the fabric on to the wearer, with familiar clammy results. Natural fibres are absorbent.

## Natural Fibres

*Cotton*  A tremendous range of fabrics, from flimsy muslin to tough canvas, are made from cotton, thus offering great variety to designers. Recently the development of certain treatments with ammonia, which does not remain in the fabric, and sometimes synthetic resins, have reduced the tendency of cotton to crease easily. Denim and corduroy are useful tough cotton products.

Cotton is grown in tropical and semi-tropical regions, and its cultivation goes back to 500 BC in India, while cotton fabrics may have been produced in Mexico as early as 5700 BC. China, the USA and the USSR are the largest producers, but Brazil, Mexico, Egypt, the Sudan, India, Pakistan and Turkey also grow large amounts. Some undesirable pesticides and chemicals are currently used in its cultivation.

Present research in cotton concerns the improvement of flame-retardant finishes and easy-care, minimum-iron fabrics. The improvement of laundry economy and the wear life of sheets is another line of research, in order to compete with man-made products.

*Linen*   Made from the fibres of the stem of the flax plant, linen is the strongest of the natural fibres, with increased strength when wet. It has all the virtues of cotton, with the added advantage that when it is laundered a micro-molecular layer is removed from each fibre, so that it comes up as new, without affecting its durability. It is naturally moth-proof, and can be woven either as fine batiste, lawn or handkerchief fabrics, or as tough materials such as are used in suitings, sheets and sailcloths. It blends very well with wool into a fabric with a soft feel and good crease-recovery, which dyes well.

Samples of linen have been found in prehistoric Swiss lake dwellings dating back for 10,000 years, and in ancient Egypt there was a well-organised linen industry. The Bible mentions it as a high-class fabric for domestic and religious use. Fine linen from Tutankhamun's tomb still survives after almost 3500 years. Before the advent of man-made fibres linen production was large-scale, but it has now shrunk; flax comprises less than 3 per cent of total textile fibres. Its production does not use harmful chemicals; the retting of the fibres is a process exploiting natural fungi and bacteria. Like cotton, linen is moisture-absorbent and conducts heat away from the body of the wearer, thus it is much in demand in hot climates.

As in the case of cotton, special finishes to render linen more crease-resistant are continually being investigated, but unfortunately all so far involve the use of non-renewable petroleum-based polymeric ingredients.

*Silk*   Most silk is spun from the cocoons of *Bombyx mori*, a moth which no longer exists in the wild; tussore silk is spun from moths of wild species. It was first cultivated in prehistoric China, and did not reach Europe until the 6th Century.

*Wool*   All wool is spun from the fleece of sheep. It cleans and wears well, and is a good insulator. If insect-proofed, it has a very long service life in such products as wool carpeting.

Wool shoddy is a valuable ingredient when making compost, but only if it is unmixed with man-made fibres, which do not rot down.

### Hair Fabrics

These are made from the coats of various animals: *Alpaca*, related to the llama of the Andes, which is made into tropical suitings, dresses and pile fabrics, but has a restricted colour range because it is difficult to bleach; *Camel hair*, which is used undyed for similar reasons, and has surface scales which enable it to be felted, for warm overcoats and dressing-gowns; *Cashmere*, the undercoat of the Tibetan goat, which has a warm, soft handle, suitable for knitwear and shawls; *Mohair*, from the Angora goat, which is made into worsted fabrics and those with a long pile; *Rabbit wool*, made from wild and Angora rabbits. It produces the very soft fibres used in knitted goods and felts, and the pure white Angora wool products. *Vicuna*, another relative of the llama, produces an expensive, fine fabric, usually retaining its natural brown, fawn or cream shades.

### Vegetable Fabrics

There are a few interesting vegetable products such as coir, from fibres in the husk of the coconut, now used for rope and matting, and the beaten bark of various tropical trees, which might perhaps with the application of new techniques be made available as renewable fabrics for designers.

### Man-made Fibres

The most common of these are acrylic, modaacrylic, elastomeric, nylon, polyester, polyethylene and polypropylene fibres. All are made from processing oil and are non-renewable.

### Recycling

Textiles can be recycled through rag-and-bone dealers, and good clothing can be sent to the various charities which resell garments.

Unwanted clothing of the most expensive kind, made from first-class material, can now be recycled through Barnardo's 'Textile Bank' (see also Fibres).

TILES

(See material concerned)

TIMBER

(See Wood)

TIMBER TREATMENT

The current practice of the industry where chemical treatment of timber to protect it from attack by fungus and insect pests is concerned is based on the assumption that all timber used in building needs to be protected chemically. Studies by the London Hazards Centre (LCH) which led to the publication of their handbook, *Toxic Treatments* (see Appendix) suggest that this assumption must be questioned. They argue that the need for chemical timber treatment arises solely from bad design practice, even when timber is directly exposed to the environment.

LCH research indicates that insect and fungal attack occur mainly in two situations. If unsuitable softwoods inadequately dried before installation are used these are very prone to attack. If timber is 'encapsulated' in the structure or by supposedly protective finishes, and subsequently becomes wet because of either bad design practice or inadequate building maintenance, it may be prevented from drying satisfactorily. Timber of suitable type and quality, correctly conditioned before installation, and correctly utilised in a building which is properly maintained is very unlikely to suffer from insect or fungal attack of any significance. On the other hand, according to Hutton & Roston Environmental Investigations Ltd (who contributed to the LHC research), even the most rigorous chemical treatment provides little more than temporary protection of structural timber, and the long-term guarantees commonly offered are in their view entirely speculative. The Centre argues that the adoption of chemical treatment as a norm is directly encouraging bad design practices in the way in which timber is used in building, and also gives a quite false sense of long-term security which may encourage inadequate maintenance. If timber becomes wet and cannot, for whatever reason, dry out quickly and completely, chemical pre-treatment will at best do little more than delay the onset of fungal and/or insect attack and may be completely ineffective.

Concern about timber treatment in the building industry context is an aspect of the general concern now being shown by environmentalists about toxic substances. Chemicals used in timber treatment do not remain as inert materials within the treated timber but degrade into gases or other substances which are gradually released into the surrounding environment. The *Toxic Treatments Handbook* lists a host of examples of toxic side effects arising both as a direct result of involvement in the treatment process and to occupants of buildings containing treated timber.

Hutton & Rostron recommend the adoption of traditional design practices, which ensure that timber in building interiors is mechanically protected from moisture and that good ventilation is available. In exterior applications, either traditional bitumen-based surface finishes or the more modern microporous paints are to be preferred to impervious coatings or paint systems, particularly to new acrylic paints which absolutely prevent timber breathing. Only in situations in which timber is permanently and unavoidably encapsulated, such as in wall plates in period houses, is there a case for the adoption of chemical solutions. However, even in such cases specialist advice should be sought to ensure that the chemicals utilised do not pose a threat to the health of the occupants of the building concerned.

TIN

Non-renewable, tin is mainly utilised in the building industry as a component of alloys such as bronze. Organic compounds of tin are also used in paints and pigments, most of which are toxic. Tin mining is a valuable source of employment in Cornwall, however, and Greens would like to see tin's use encouraged for non-polluting purposes, as its extraction is not in general environmentally destructive.

TITANIUM

This material is difficult to extract, and therefore energy-consuming. It is used in the building industry mainly for special fittings, being as strong as steel but 45 per cent lighter; twice as strong as aluminium, but 60 per cent heavier. Titanium dioxide is a non-toxic substance used in white paint for its excellent opacity. From the environmental viewpoint, this is a material the use of which should in general be avoided. Unfortunately it is at present a vital ingredient in the manufacture of catalytic convertors to render cars less polluting.

The mining of titanium in Norway results in large residues, which at the moment are tipped into Norwegian fjords, with disastrous effects on fishing – a major industry – and wildlife. Environmentalists feel that spoil of this kind should be used in some way, perhaps, as aggregates in building processes (see Metals).

TRACE ORGANICS

This term covers the whole range of carbon-based substances which are at the heart of Green concern about the pollution of our drinking water and food. It includes pesticide residues; the toxic by-products of industrial processes; hydrocarbons dumped after use, leaked from storage tanks or accidentally spilled; the breakdown products of solvents and other volatile materials brought back to the earth in rain, and substances formed naturally during the breakown of, for example, wood in water. Trace organics reach our food chain partly through drinking water; partly through the irrigation of crops by contaminated water, and partly through their concentration in the flesh of cattle, sheep, pigs, poultry and fish.

It is only relatively recently that analytical techniques have become widely available which can trace the minute quantities of trace organics increasingly present in the environment. At first it was thought that, as some of them arise naturally, we need not worry about potential health risks at the tiny concentrations so far registered. But we now know that as a result of human interference in the ecosystem even natural organic toxins are currently arising in rivers and underground aquifers in much larger quantities than before, and that the quantity and diversity of man-made toxic organics and their breakdown products in water are far greater than had previously been suspected. A large number of such substances are cumulative in the body; some are known to be carcinogenic, and others cause liver and kidney damage. As a result, trace organics are likely to become one of the main topics of environmental pollution concern during the next few years. In the present context, as the building industry contributes heavily to the accumulation of these substances in the environment (see, for example, Preservatives and Solvents), it behoves all those working in building, design and the selection of building materials to bear trace organics in mind.

TREES

Every fresh planting of an indigenous tree is an environmental step forward. They contribute towards cleansing the air; they provide valuable compost material; they become rich ecosystems for wildlife and they enhance the view. Certain trees, such as weeping willows, should be planted well away from drainage systems and houses, which can be damaged by the roots. Limes and sycamores should not be planted in streets or car parks, as they drip a sticky exudate, and sycamore seedlings are troublesome. The native field maple (*Acer campestre*) or the London plane (*Platanus hybrida*) are good subsitutes for the sycamore. Smaller native trees, suitable for gardens, and good for wildlife, include the berry-producing rowan or mountain ash (*Sorbus aucuparia*); the wild cherry (*Prunus avium*); and the various crab apples (*Malus spp.*), the fruit of which is attractive to winter migrant birds.

Native trees and shrubs are more valuable environmentally than exotic species, because they are already part of the ecological web of insect and bird life. Dozens of species of moth caterpillars eat the leaves of our native oaks, feeding the local birds in turn, whereas no native insect larvae would feed, for example, on magnolia.

# U

UPHOLSTERY

Traditional upholstery techniques, which were based entirely on the use of long-lasting, natural and renewable materials, took it for granted that eventually these would need refurbishing. Most contemporary upholstery materials are accepted as for one-time use, and the design of modern furniture renders repair and refurbishment difficult or impossible. The Green viewpoint challenges furniture designers to devise ways of adapting traditional materials: horse-hair, natural textiles and the like, so that once again furniture can be reconditioned and refurbished.

The use of flexible foam in furniture is affected by the regulations which began to come into force in November 1988 (see Rubber; Foam).

# V

**VARNISH**            (See Finishes)

**VENTILATION**        (See Air-conditioning; Insulation)

**VERMICULITE**        A non-renewable material similar to mica, found in various forms in rocks and sometimes as small particles in soil. When rapidly heated to about 300°C, it expands twenty times and becomes very light. Useful in lightweight concretes, plasters, insulation, packing, soil conditioning, as a starting medium for seeds and as a filler in paper, paint and plastics. So far no renewable subsitute has been found.

**VERNACULAR ARCHITECTURE AND CONSTRUCTION**        Vernacular styles in building construction and detail have developed from the localised use of readily available materials and the reinterpretation of particular stylistic fashions. Period details which in some cases fell out of general use centuries ago for major buildings may be retained in localised use to the present day. Unfortunately, local vernacular styles and materials are often either not recognised by developers or thought to be incompatible with efficient modern practice and, as a result, efforts to preserve our heritage of localised architectural detail tend to be confined to conservation areas and national parks. Even in such places, the wide use of nationally standardised building components and materials is still destroying local traditions which may have survived from Georgian or earlier times. This process began in Victorian times, when in the process of the 'Gothic Revival' styles from many different design periods were intermixed without care for their roots. It continues today with 'traditional' styles of window frames, roof materials and components, paving and brickwork and surface finishes being adopted for domestic and commercial construction which have little or no relevance to local traditions.

From an environmental viewpoint, such watering down of long-established local styles of construction can be viewed in two ways. Visually, the peculiar richness of local character unique to so many villages, towns and cities throughout Britain is being progessively destroyed and this must be regretted. However, vernacular use of particular materials and styles also arose for sound practical reasons which are often totally relevant to current Green thinking. For instance, the use of locally-available materials reduces transport energy cost. But it should also be remembered that specific styles, materials and construction methods came into vernacular usage because they were found to be efficient and durable in local weather conditions. In other words, if the Green philosophy of building for durability is generally adopted, it is likely to result in much greater interest in localised vernacular design at every level from the general approach to scale and orientation to details of external joinery, roofing and walling materials and actual methods of construction.

In recent years we have seen a trend away from uniformity in design, especially where estate housing is concerned, but houses still tend to be built in 'national' styles which are a melange of elements from different parts of the country and have more to do with a company image than sensitivity to local traditions. It is strange to see houses being built in County Durham which have a character some would think more appropriate to Dorset. The housing estates of London commuterland could have been designed absolutely anywhere and make little or no visual reference to the individuality of Kentish, Hertfordshire or Essex towns and villages.

Local Planning Authorities do not generally seem to be concerned to insist on an attempt to perpetuate local vernacular, other than in a very superficial sense. Overworked listed buildings officers usually have enough trouble preventing those involved in 'restoring' listed properties incorporating cheap standard windows and other components in them, without worrying about the wider problem of persuading builders and developers generally that much of their work is actually destroying the very individuality of local character which persuades incomers to pay such high prices for their production-line products in the first place. If the buildings they were creating had real design merit, either visually or in terms of constructional durability, the situation might be easier to tolerate. Some have, but they are the outstanding exceptions.

VOLATILE
SUBSTANCES                      (See Solvents)


VYNIL                              (See Floorings; Plastics)

**WALLPAPER**    (See Finishes; Paper)

**WALLS**    (See material concerned)

**WASTE**    To Greens, this is a word which symbolises sin. There is no such thing as useless waste. Some of the most toxic substances are actually a richer source of certain materials than the natural source, so that some industries are considering the mining of infilled waste for rare metals. Many of the wastes we produce can be recycled within the home, office or factory where they are produced; waste heat is an example. Others, such as compostable food residues, are of interest to gardeners, pig-owners and for natural fertilisers. Facilities for recycling glass, plastics, newsprint, metals and furniture are already beginning to exist, and are spreading. In some areas it is possible to recycle domestic appliances and clothing. Within industry and commerce, recycling is beginning to be seen as an actual or potential positive item on the balance sheet, whereas a decade ago waste was something you hoped to dispose of as cheaply as possible and forget.

Much commercial and domestic waste, if not recyclable, can be used as fuel in specially-designed furnaces, and the resulting energy used. There is considerable scope for district incineration plants providing district heating as a by-product; for building complexes which derive much of their energy input from their own wastes; for the use of one factory's waste as a raw material for another factory nearby. The vital first step is to separate waste: once mixed, its potential value is drastically reduced. Greens would therefore put an end to the catch-all waste bin and switch to on-site sorting. The challenge to architects and designers is to take the initiative in proposing on-site environment-friendly uses for waste, and ensure that toxic substances are rendered safe within the confines of the originating establishment.

*Agricultural Wastes*    A new generation of anaerobic digesters has transformed the prospect for farm waste treatment practice (see Appendix). Expensive and clumsy reinforced-concrete sewage treatment plants can now be replaced by prefabricated double-skinned foam-filled glass-reinforced plastic vessels. These roughly halve the cost of digester systems, can be installed within a few weeks and are already being used in a few farms, abbatoirs and water authorities. They are tailored to the needs of the user, and produce both agricultural fertiliser and methane gas, which can be used to fuel the system, provide hot water, to heat premises or to dry out grain.

Interesting examples of the new techniques are: the sludge digestion plant being installed on the island of Sark, which will treat the septic tank waste from 500 people, rising to 1500 in the summer months; the Bishops Castle abbatoir in Shropshire, which produces methane gas which is stored in a sausage-shaped metre butyl gas bag, by which the gas fuels the boiler, switching back to fuel oil when a sensor detects falling pressure in the bag. The excess gas produced at the weekend is compressed and used as a vehicle fuel. The other products are a peat-like fibre and a low solids liquid, both of which are valuable as fertilisers. Also of interest is the Cistercian monastery at Portglenone, Northern Ireland, where an anaerobic digestion system and fibre separation plant produce biogas for central heating and grain drying, as well as an organic compost which is bagged and sold. The separated liquids from the digester form the basis of an organically-grown wheat enterprise. Both the abbatoir and the monastery won Pollution Abatement Technology Awards in 1986.

*Coal-Mining Wastes*    The spoil-heaps created by underground mining vary in content. When formed of shale, it is marketed under the name 'Minestone' (see Appendix), for which there are many outlets, such as its use in embankments, ramps and the like. It can also be stabilised with cement for building uses. Old spoil-heaps of low-grade coal can now be reclaimed and used. Other types of spoil are sometimes used for infilling on mudflats, as in the landing area for hovercraft at Ramsgate. However, transport costs are a barrier, and most spoil which cannot be used locally is used as infill after opencast mining, restored by landscaping, or, at worst, tipped into the sea, as is seen on the coast of County Durham.

*Domestic Waste*   The composition of household waste was investigated by INCPEN, and found to be 37 per cent plastics, metal and glass in roughly equal proportions; 16.3 per cent textiles; 14.6 per cent paper; 9.6 per cent dust and cinders; 6.7 per cent 'putrescents', mostly vegetable matter, and the remaining 15.8 per cent of unclassified odds and ends. Of this, if local authorities provided appropriate facilities, most of the paper, some of the plastics, most of the metal, all of the glass and most of the textiles could be reclaimed and the energy used. It is from the 'putrescents' that methane gas is generated on waste tips, often with highly dangerous results. Yet this gas, properly managed, could be used for cooking and heating, and is so used in parts of India, Nepal and China. The retrospective fitting of gas extraction systems is difficult, but in newly-established infill sites extraction equipment can be installed at the outset, and the methane extracted for positive use, for commercial or domestic heating, rather than becoming an explosive menace.

Local authorities vary widely in their waste-disposal efficiency, but most is still disposed of in filling up holes. Ferrous metal is sometimes collected, a few methane schemes are going ahead, some pulverised waste is used as a commercial feeedstock and there are some glass, plastic and tin recovery schemes operating. While a number of waste-disposal authorities incinerate waste, few use the heat generated; instead they cool the product with river water, which is thus polluted.

An interesting development is fluidised-bed combustion, which can be used to incinerate waste material, including even sewage slurry. With the use of combined heat and power, this process could produce energy for heating.

The National Council for Voluntary Organisations (see Appendix) estimates that as a nation we throw away £750 million annually in recyclable materials. While pressure is put on local authorities to make new recycling provisions, or to improve provisions already made, builders and designers can do much to make disposal of household rubbish less wasteful.

In the UK, mechanised waste-disposal exists in embryo: trial schemes have been carried out at Doncaster, Byker and Chichester. In these schemes, the immediately recyclable waste (metals, glass, plastics, and paper and board) is first recovered, and the remainder is processed to make fuel pellets. This waste-disposal fuel (WDF) is lighter and bulkier per therm than coal, and transporting a given amount of energy per therm therefore costs more, but it can now be produced to suit a wide range of outlets. It can be used unmixed in a fluidised-bed system (see Fuel), and burns satisfactorily in coal-burning appliances. There are many possibilities for in-house applications for local authorities such as swimming-pools, schools and offices, as well as for types of district heating. The situation on going to press is that few local authorities in the UK have installed or are planning to install mechanical waste-sorting equipment for recycling waste.

Ingenious machines have been developed during these experiments, and there is still scope for inventive mechanical engineers here.

One of the major problems has been the moisture content in domestic waste; commercial and industrial waste is easier to turn into fuel pellets after sorting. If there were facilities in our kitchens for domestic waste to be divided easily into metal, paper, glass and organic materials, and municipal waste collection continued this process, the whole national position would be transformed and recycling would become a much less expensive option.

### Hazardous Waste

Britain's £5-billion-a-year hazardous-waste business is unique in Western Europe in being left almost entirely to private enterprise. Its imports of hazardous waste have increased from 5000 tonnes in 1985 to 52,000 tonnes, in addition to 128,000 tonnes of less hazardous rubbish. Waste 'brokers' proliferate, and the natural tendency is for the cheapest site to be chosen. This, remarks the 1988 Report of the Hazardous Waste Inspectorate, is likely to be the one with the lowest standards. It comments that the ideal principle in the disposal of hazardous waste would be that of producer responsibility.

The Inspectorate currently has only a staff of five to cover the whole country, and in 1988 the Chief Inspector resigned in frustration.

A problem which has recently arisen in waste disposal is that of aerosols, which can explode, and which destroy the ozone layer. Specialist plants are to be constructed for their disposal.

The Report on Hazardous Waste mentions that hospital design should include efficient incinerators kept at a steady high temperature, and that there should be no storage of waste material before incineration. Ideally, incinerators should be coupled to a heat recovery system.

**Waste Heat**
Energy wasted through inefficient fuel utilisation is a loss to the user and the environment, and there is tremendous potential in recovering heat lost in this way. Waste heat may be graded as: *Flue Gases*, which offer great potential for recovery if the temperature is high; *Liquid or Vapour Streams*: also great potential, and, when condensed, latent heat also recoverable; *Convective and Radiant Heat* (from walls and exteriors of equipment), if collected, can be used for space heating or preheating air; *Cooling Water*: heat can be exchanged with incoming fresh water; *Chilling Water*: this causes heat loss, which can sometimes be utilised. There is also heat loss in products leaving a hot process and in hot gaseous and liquid effluents, which can sometimes be reclaimed. The various heat recovery systems include shell, tube and plate type heat exchangers, run-round coil systems, recuperators, regenerators, and heat wheels, pipes and pumps (see Appendix).

Industry in the UK uses about 1700 PJ a year, of which some 600 PJ is used by the high-temperature process industries: Iron and Steel; Iron Casting; Aluminium; Copper; Glass; Potteries; Bricks and Ceramics. A study on behalf of the Energy Efficiency Office showed that in 1982 some 90 PJ were wasted, lost as hot gases above 400°C. The Iron and Steel industry is the biggest user of energy and the largest generator of clean waste heat. Much of this heat can be recovered, partly by cutting down waste at the source and partly by devices such as heat exchangers, waste-heat boilers, fluidised-bed systems and regenerators (see Appendix and details under Metals; Glass, etc.).

PJ stands for petajoule. One PJ equals 10 to the 15 joules, a joule being a basic energy unit (1 Kwh = 3600000J = 3.6MJ). Thus PJ are large energy units suitable for expressing energy consumption a million times greater than the amounts which are of interest to heating engineers.

### Waste Paper

The waste-paper market in the UK lacks cohesion and organisation. It could benefit from copying the system devised in the Netherlands which has helped to stabilise the supply and price of raw materials. There the largest waste-paper-consuming mills have entered into an agreement with the waste-paper trade about closer cooperation, and an independent company has been formed which is empowered to buy buffer stocks at times of excess, and release them at times of shortage and high prices (see also Paper).

WATER

A decade ago we took it for granted that our drinking water supply was safely pure. But now our contemporary pattern of living has caught up with us. It has polluted and is polluting the rivers and artesian sources from which we draw our industrial and domestic supplies; what we drink now is a chemical soup of contaminants and substances added during treatment. Nitrates and phosphates, in the first place, cause eutrophication through excessive algae growth. The slimy algae fill rivers and the fish die. But in addition even more dangerous substances, very difficult to trace and treat, are now present (see Trace Organics).

Drinking water standards are laid down by an EC directive, backed up by guidelines published by the Department of the Environment (DOE). In theory the recent Water Act places the supply authorities under an legal obligation to provide water which meets the EC standards. In practice the Act contains loopholes which permit authorities to supply water at a lower standard without fear of prosecution. This is partly because there is at present no technology to deal with many types of contamination which are now commonplace, and partly because the DOE's guidelines, while theoretically laying down levels 'based on expert medical advice', up to which water need not actually be cut off, tacitly permit higher levels of certain substances than are laid down by the EC.

*Nitrates and Phosphates*   Unfortunately attention has been focused on this subject rather than on pollution by other more toxic contaminants. Nitrate and phosphate levels in drinking water do indeed commonly exceed those laid down by the EC, especially in areas of intensive grain monoculture where water supplies are largely drawn from underground aquifers. Permeable strata there retain nitrates leached out of the soil from fertiliser, sewage sludge and runoff from silage clamps. Phosphates come from various detergents. It has taken twenty-five years for nitrates to arrive in boreholes at high concentrations, but by the same principle it will take a long time to get rid of them. It is easy to trace and measure nitrates, but we still do not know whether they are a real menace to health. In theory the authorities could be sued for supplying water containing nitrates at higher levels than directed by the EC, but the DOE is correct to state that there is no definite health reason for taking drastic steps to decrease nitrate levels. As the only technique known for doing so has the effect of creating water salinity, this is fortunate.

*Other Pollutants*   Pesticide residues and pollution by toxic trace organics are a more serious matter (see Trace Organics). These include known carcinogens; the World Health Organisation stated in 1985 that 80 per cent of all human cancers can be attributed to substances in the air we breathe and the water we drink. Many of these pollutants accumulate slowly in the body, and as their detection involves highly specialised and expensive analytical techniques, we know little about their extent and effect.

The EC directive set a limit of five parts per million for the *total* pollution by contaminants of drinking water, because when the legislation was drafted this figure was regarded as effectively meaning zero. But recent techniques have enabled scientists to detect parts per trillion, which has opened a frightening new vista, bearing in mind the cumulative build-up of some trace organics. Additional guidelines issued by the DOE to the water authorities, moreover, ignore the EC figure, setting out a series of recommended upper limits for some forty specific substances. These guidelines actually suggest acceptable contamination levels by single substances of up to six times the EC limit for *all* such toxins, and ignore the EC 'total content' rule completely. It is true that no effective means exist at present for removing trace organics from the water supply, and also that no reliable method of testing total pesticide content has so far been devised. The various trace organics now found in drinking water extend to some 600 substances used in pesticides, and residues from more than 100 industrial and commercial processes. But the water authorities only publish test figures for a few of the substances which appear on the DOE list, and the tests themselves are very limited in scope and frequency.

The Green attitude is that urgent steps must be taken to reduce the usage of polluting substances, and to ban the more toxic ones at once. At the same time, industries and companies producing residues such as solvents, exotic compounds of chlorine, fluoride and heavy metals must be compelled to neutralise or recycle them on the premises, at source. Meanwhile, Greens would invest heavily in research into improving methods of analysing and understanding these dangerous pollutants, and creating efficient means for dealing with them. But even if these steps were to be taken at once by an enlightened government, it would be a long time before we could all be sure of drinking pure water once again (see also Energy; Waste).

WATER FILTERS     In-house water treatment systems are for the present the only practical means of dealing with water pollution. It has to be accepted, however, that no technology exists at present for removing or even reducing levels of toxic trace elements from drinking water. Existing water treatment does to some extent reduce contaminants, and water authorities mix supplies to dilute contamination as much as possible. Water filters or purifiers can to a limited extent help in potability, but their limitations should be understood.

Consumers are concerned, of course, about the taste, appearance, turbidity and heavy metal content of water. Caterers and drink dispensers, as well as domestic users, want to be able to make a decent cup of tea or coffee with potable water. Much interest therefore exists in obtaining reliable water filters and purifiers. There is no legal standard by which these can be tested, and many of those offered are of questionable value. Some could even be dangerous in certain circumstances, allowing the growth of bacterial communities. There is also a possibility that some water authorities will cooperate with certain commercial suppliers in the sale of filters in future; an arrangement profitable to both, but not necessarily of benefit to the consumer. The following standard rules are therefore suggested for future water filters and purifiers:

1   The system should be fail-safe; that is, the flow of water through the filter should cease if the primary filter system fails, becomes clogged with residues or is infected with colonies of bacteria. The filter should not support the growth or release of those bacteria which cause diarrhoea or enteric disease.

2   The system should remove those bacteria and other harmful organisms which are not effectively destroyed or controlled by chlorine or other bacteria-controlling techniques.

3   Throughout its normal lifespan the filter should remove 95 per cent of all organic pollutants, chlorine and chlorinated hydrocarbons.

4   The removal of submicronic particles of suspended matter, including asbestos fibres, heavy metals, excessive amounts of iron or hydrogen sulphide, should be guaranteed.

5   Dissolved minerals beneficial to health should not be removed by the filter.

6   The filter or purifier should add no substance, including salt or gases, by ion exchange or other process to the water.

7  The system should be warranted as suitable for domestic, intermittent usage.

8  The system should incorporate an automatic indication when service, or component replacement, is necessary.

The testing and approval standards currently being considered by the DOE and water authorities are not as stringent as the above, possibly because the products of the leading manufacturers would be disqualified by them. But consumers may well feel that it is better to be awkwardly strict about standards than to risk health hazards in drinking water.

WAX                  (See Finishes)

WINDOWS              (See Air-Conditioning; Eco-Architecture)

WOOD                 Potentially the ultimate environment-friendly building material. Grown and harvested on a planned basis it is an indefinitely renewable resource. Moreover, during their growth trees capture substantial amounts of carbon dioxide from the air and convert it into wood, giving off oxygen freely as a by-product. Managed deciduous forests, which provide a rich ecological network, can make an immeasurable contribution to redeeming the environment, and offer an ideal use for areas where industry or agriculture are not present or not desirable.

Native trees provide habitats for other species, and are an essential component in many ecosystems. The land surfaces of the earth were once largely covered by forests, and their removal has contributed to changing our climate, as for instance in the once richly-forested Sahara. It has also caused erosion, which in turn produces the flooding, mudslides and landslides which have become so tragically familiar, and has resulted in the near disappearance of many of our companion species, such as the once common woodland species of butterflies in the UK: the fritillaries, the white admirals and the hair-streaks. In some parts of the world, especially the rainforests of the tropics, trees are an irreplaceable store of known and as yet unknown medical remedies and foods. Sustainable timber is also a potential raw material for many uses now supplied by non-renewable products.

Historically, timber has been regarded by the building and furniture industries as an infinite resource to be exploited without thought for the safety of future supplies. Until relatively recently, it always seemed that as one forest area was worked out another would be discovered. Tragically late, we are now realising how wrong this attitude was.

Britain was once covered with mixed woodlands, but by the end of the 17th Century these had been all but destroyed by the same process of spreading agriculture, urbanisation and timber exploitation which is now afflicting the Amazon Basin, West Africa, the Far East and the islands of the Pacific. Part of the cost of creating much of the classical furniture and interior joinery of the 18th and early-19th Centuries, and later the factories and warehouses of Victorian industry, was the utter destruction of easily accessible coastal forests in the West Indies, West Africa and the Pacific. Within living memory, sources of hardwoods in Central and South America and several central African countries have been completely worked out for commercial purposes and the forests involved turned into exhausted and unproductive thorn scrub and savanna.

The first glimmerings can now be seen of an understanding that unless we change the way we exploit timber as a resource the result will be a catastrophe of unimaginable proportions. Though use of timber, and tropical timbers in particular, is by no means the only or even the main cause of worldwide deforestation, it plays a vital role, because roads opened up into virgin areas during the search for commercial logwood are usually the first step to other forms of exploitation, setting into motion the cycle of destruction with which we are all familiar.

Unfortunately, in many countries which could supply large quantities of excellent temperate hardwoods and softwoods, continued exploitation of tropical timber resources is being directly encouraged by poor forestry and timber conversion practices. Anyone involved in handling softwoods, especially from northern European sources, finds that the quality of such timber, by the time it reaches the end user, has dropped dramatically during the last three or four decades. Even fifty years ago, softwoods were regarded as structural materials of choice, whereas they are now treated as a cheap and unreliable option, to be replaced whenever possible by structural steelwork, manufactured boards or other non-renewable materials.

It is to the credit of some North American timber growers and suppliers that they are working hard to change current attitudes towards the role of both soft and hardwood temperate timbers, within the building industry, but they are hampered by both specifiers and users, as well as by the tendency of the timber trade in this country to resist changes in practice. In the United States there is a long tradition of family-owned managed woodlands which are capable of supplying large quantities of many hardwoods of consistently high quality. We are also beginning to see imports into the UK of specialised high-quality softwoods, such as Southern Yellow Pine. This is an excellent wood for high-quality general joinery, and is now imported in container-loads of sawn timber pre-dried to guaranteed moisture content levels.

The answer to the problem is not a total ban in Britain on the use of tropical hardwoods, but changes in buying practices and utilisation, as suggested below.

Many Third World countries depend heavily on the income from timber sales for vital hard currency. Several, such as Indonesia and Kenya, and to some extent Brazil, have attempted to switch to managed forest policies, but the practice of buying tropical timber as logs for processing and converting in Europe and Japan, and especially of using tropical logwood as a cheap raw material for board production, is effectively preventing such a change. The following changes could solve this problem completely within as little as five years, and designers could make a valuable contribution to bringing them about by inserting appropriate clauses in specifications relating to timber use:

1   Cease using tropical hardwoods immediately in all applications in which the substitution of temperate hardwoods and softwoods is possible.

This applies to virtually all building joinery, such as window frames, staircases and standard doors. Tropical timber should be used exclusively in premium and specialised situations, and in specifying such timbers it should be a contractual condition that the supplier guarantees the timber as being from a renewably managed forest source. This guarantee should be supported by secondary evidence from a government source or official equivalent.

2   Insert a specification clause in all contracts involving the use of tropical hardwoods stating that the timber is certified as being the product of managed, sustainable forestry by the relevant government agency in the country of origin.

Some timber importers, responding to increasing concern about tropical timber within the building industry, have begun to negotiate supply contracts with Third World government agencies. This is a first step towards protecting the source of supply, but in some cases the dependability of the response is questionable. Nevertheless, there is hope that certification would at least rule out supplies from areas where no change to sustainable forestry is contemplated.

3   Cease all imports of tropical logwood.

All conversion of logs to semi-finished timber and veneers should take place in the country of origin. This raises the hard currency income of the producer country and encourages local merchants to invest in managed forestry.

4   Cease all imports of plywood and other board products made of tropical hardwoods.

The use of tropical hardwoods as a component in plywoods of other types of boards for building purposes is an appalling waste of valuable timber, which should be conserved for special uses. Many UK board importers and suppliers are making an effort to improve the quality of plywoods made from timbers from temperate sources, and are developing new board products from these sources. Many of these new boards have characteristics which render them particularly useful for dry construction and partitioning techniques, offering significant savings in energy both during and after manufacture.

5   Apply the above rules to imports of products from Third World countries.

At present Japan is the principal importer of unconverted tropical logwood and board products incorporating tropical timbers. Some proportion of this material is re-exported after conversion or as part of manufactured products.

The list given below should be read in conjunction with the recommendations set out above.

**Timbers we should avoid using**

The following timbers are either in immediate danger of extinction for commercial purposes or are not available from any source country where sustainable forestry practices have been adopted. This list is not definitive, and as names used in the trade are not precise, it is safer to assume that, in the absence of absolutely reliable contractual guarantees to the contrary, any hardwood which is not grown in North America or Europe is from unmanaged and therefore unsustainable forest sources. Of course, if the four recommendations set out above were to be followed, the situation concerning the following timbers could gradually be transformed.

| Timber | Source |
| --- | --- |
| Afrormosia | Africa |
| Abura | Africa |
| Cedar (Honduras) | Central and South America |
| Ebony | Africa, India, Sri Lanka |
| Gaboon/Okoume | West Africa |
| Iroko | West & East Africa |
| Jelutong | Malaysia, Indonesia |
| Kapur | Malaysia, Indonesia |
| Kempas | Malaysia |
| Keruing/Gurjun | Malaysia |
| Mahogany | Africa, Central and South America, West Indies, Philippines |
| Meranti | Malaysia |
| Merbau | Malaysia, Indonesia |
| Okwen | West Africa |
| Ovangkol | West Africa |
| Padauk | Asia, Pacific Islands, Africa          (*contd*) |

Table (*contd*)

| Timber | Source |
| --- | --- |
| Pau Marfim | Brazil |
| Ramin | Malaysia, Indonesia |
| Red Peroba | Brazil |
| Rosewood | Brazil |
| Sapele | West and Central Africa |
| Utile | Africa |
| Wenge | Central and West Africa |

The following are other tropical hardwoods in limited supply or only available as veneers. They are, in the majority of cases, endangered species:

Abura, African Walnut, Afzelia, Agba, Anigre, Avodire, Etimoe, Greywood (Indian), Guarea, Idigbo, Izombe, Khaya, Limba, Makore, Moabi, Opepe, Paldao, Satinwood, Zebrano.

## Timbers which can be freely used

*Tropical Hardwoods*

| Timber | Source |
| --- | --- |
| Greenheart | Guyana |
| Rubberwood | Malaysia |
| Teak | Some sustainably managed forests now exist in Java Thailand and Burma (see Appendix) |

*Temperate Hardwoods*   The following list contains woods which have characteristics which make them ideal as replacements for tropical hardwoods, especially for use in external joinery and window frames. Native hardwoods often have a greater inherent resistance to pests and weathering than the exotic timbers now widely used. The timbers listed below are increasingly becoming available at competitive prices and in commercial quantities.

| Timber | Source |
|---|---|
| Alder | Europe, North-eastern America |
| Apple | Europe, North America |
| Ash | Europe |
| Ash, Olive | North America |
| Aspen | North America |
| Beech | Europe, North America |
| Birch | Europe, North America |
| Blackbean | North America |
| Black Walnut | North America |
| Cherry | Europe, North America |
| Chestnut | Europe |
| Elm | Europe, North America |
| Hickory | North America |
| Lime | Europe |
| Maple | North America |
| Oak | Europe, North America, Japan |
| Olivewood | Europe |
| Pear | Europe |
| Plane | Europe |
| Poplar | Europe |
| Queensland Maple | Australasia |
| Sycamore | Europe, North America |
| Tulipwood | North America |
| Willow | Europe |

*Softwoods*   The list of softwoods from Europe, Siberian Russia and North America is potentially very long and most are not sold by name. However, the following are worth special investigation, either because of their unique appearance or because they are available to the trade in qualities suitable for high-performance joinery.

| Timber | Source | |
|---|---|---|
| Baltic Pine (selected) | Europe | |
| Cedar (Lebanon) | Europe, Middle East | |
| Columbian Pine | North America | |
| Douglas Fir | Europe, North America | *(contd)* |

Table (*contd*)

| Timber | Source |
| --- | --- |
| Hemlock | North America |
| Larch | Europe |
| Oregon Pine | North America |
| Parana Pine | South America |
| Southern Yellow Pine | North America |
| Spruce | Europe |
| Western Red Cedar | North America |
| Yew | Europe |

The attention of Green designers should also begin to turn to the desirability of timber from renewable sources for building.

Scandinavian countries have long been aware of the value of timber for domestic buildings. Now that we know more about techniques for dealing with moisture and other problems when designing wood houses, there is no reason why we should not move from the use of brick and concrete to sustainable timber sources for domestic dwellings. This would be a gigantic environmental step forward. Well-built and tested timber houses are energy-efficient, flexible for later alterations and respond organically to outside conditions (see Appendix). The main obstacles to progress in this area are the entrenched attitudes of building societies and banks (with the honourable exception of the Ecology Building Society – see Appendix) on financing timber housing, and the resistance of the building industry and its suppliers. Pioneer builders and self-build advisers are springing up all over the UK, and it is to be hoped that some building society will soon join their ranks.

A recent welcome development has been the planting of coppices on land 'set aside' by farmers. This is strongly supported by Greens, as it provides sustainable timber for building and other uses, and the twigs and leaves can be used for biomass.

Massive tree planting in cities would make a major contribution to reducing the greenhouse effect, but the higher floor space densities of contemporary designs have tended against this development. A large forest tree – oak, beech, maple, ash or hornbeam –

can take some 10 kg of carbon dioxide out of circulation in a single day. A proportion is respired at night, but even so some 7 kg less 'greenhouse gas' is left in circulation at the end of twenty-four hours.

To be of significant use, major trees must be chosen; London is now benefiting from the mature plane trees planted around the turn of the century. The required space for each planting is a shallow cylinder, depending on the size of the species. Oaks and beeches, which have a canopy diameter of about 15 metres require a root run of 16 metres or more, and about 2 metres deep. At least the central $5 \times 5$ metres of the surrounding pavement should be open to the elements and gridded over to protect the soil from trampling. Services should not be run through the roots, though they grow satisfactorily around small existing pipes. There is gradual recognition of the value of trees on new city sites, but it is a sad comment that when well-grown trees are included, as in the Broadgate site in the City of London, they have to be purchased abroad, as the techniques, pioneered in the UK, have not been developed here.

Along major arterial roads, tree planting which does not shade nearby houses makes a significant contribution both to the landscape and the micro-climate. Landscaped buffer zones between industrial and domestic sites, planted with trees, render mixed zoning acceptable.

When building on a site where existing trees are to be retained it is important not to cut off the root plates, alter the water table near the trees or change the soil level on the trunks, otherwise they will eventually die.

WOOD
PRESERVATIVES

All chemicals used in timber treatment are toxic to some degree. because by their very nature they need to kill organisms and to persist. The least hazardous, chosen by the Nature Conservancy Council because they are less harmful to bats, which are protected animals, are treatments based on permethrin, and boron compounds. However, precautions should be taken even when applying these, as permethrins have been associated with nervous system damage and allergies, and the organic metal compounds, of which boron is one, are nerve poisons. It is better when possible to avoid the use of preservatives altogether, by good ventilation, the use of airbricks, and avoiding moisture entry through bridged damp-proof courses. These measures will avoid dry rot. Proper maintenance and regular decorating will stop wet rot. Infestation can be avoided by regular inspection and maintenance; wood-worm is only a menace when still active. The main need for preservation is in exposed timbers such as roof timbers, when the least hazardous preparations should be used (see Timber Treatment).

**WOOD TREATMENT**    (See Timber Treatment)

ZINC (See Metals)

# Appendix

| | |
|---|---|
| ALUMINIUM RECYCLING | An information pack can be obtained from: ARC–P, PO Box 57, Newport, Gwent NPI 9XS. |
| ANAEROBIC DIGESTERS (Sewage and Waste) | Details available from: Farm Gas Ltd., Industrial Estate, Bishops Castle, Shropshire SY9 5AQ. |
| BATS | The Nature Conservancy Council issues a free leaflet, *Bats in Roofs, a Guide for Surveyors*, and a booklet, *Bats in Houses* for £0.60. Both are available from the Council at Northminster House, Peterborough PE1 1UA (0733 40345). |
| BIODEGRADABLE PLASTICS | Research being carried out by David Barstow, Marlborough Polymers Ltd., Elta House, Yarm Road, Stockton-on-Tees, Cleveland TS18 3RX. |
| BUILDING SOCIETY | The Ecology Building Society, 18 Station Road, Cross Hills, Keighley, WYBD 7EH (0535 35933). |
| COMBINED HEAT AND POWER | A list of suppliers of CHP systems can be obtained from: ETSU, Building 156, Harwell Laboratory, Oxon OX11 0RA. |
| DUCTED AIR | A firm which has already built an eco-friendly headquarters with a ducted air system is: Conder Group, Kings Worthy Court, Winchester, Hants, SO23 7QA (0962 88222). |

| | |
|---|---|
| FLUIDISED-BED COMBUSTION | A list of UK manufacturers of equipment for this process can be obtained from the National Coal Board, Hobart House, Grosvenor Place, London SW1X 7AE. |
| HAZARDS IN MANUFACTURE AND USE | The London Hazards Centre, 308 Grays Inn Road, London WC1X 8DS (01-837 5605), specialises in providing facts concerning the dangers of certain materials, both to workers in production and users. For further details see the Centre's handbook, *Toxic Treatments*. Information can also be obtained from Hutton & Rostron Environmental Investigations Ltd., Netley House, Gomshall, Guildford, Surrey GU5 9QA. |
| KITCHEN FURNITURE | Two useful sources of information are available. The general picture is covered in depth by *A Hard Wood Story*, by F. Nectoux and N. Dudley. If you wish to know sources of supply in your own area of furniture made from wood from a sustainable source, *The Good Wood Guide* will tell you. Both are available from Friends of the Earth, 26–8 Underwood Street, London N1 7JQ (01 490 1555), prices on request. |
| LEATHER | For further information: British Leather Confederation, Leather Trades House, Kings Park Road, Moulton Park, Northampton NN3 IJD. |
| LINEN | For further information: The Irish Linen Guild, Lambeg Road, Lisburn, Northern Ireland BT27 4RL. |
| METHANE GAS | An example of the industrial use of methane is the Shanks and McEwan Brickworks at Stewartby; an example of its agricultural use is Farm Gas at Bishops Castle (see above). |
| MINESTONE APPLICATIONS | Minestone Executive, National Coal Board, Hobart House, Grosvenor Place, London SW1X 7AE. |
| NATURAL RADIATION | Estimation of Natural Radiation. See *Nature*, 28 July 1988, vol. 334 p. 338. |

| | |
|---|---|
| NOISE POLLUTION | Full details of precautions against most types are given in the excellent booklet *Sound Control for Homes*, Report No. 115, issued by CIRIA (Construction Industry Research and Information Association), 6 Storey's Gate, London SW1P 3AU (01-222 8891). |
| PAPER PULP PRODUCTS | For details of the dangers of bleaching pulp *The Sanitary Protection Scandal* can be obtained for £6.40 including postage from: Women's Environmental Network, 287 City Road, London EC1V 1LA. |
| PLASTICS WASTE RECYCLING COMPANIES | A full list can be obtained from The Plastics and Rubber Advisory Service, 5 Belgrave Square, London SW1X 8PH. At the time of going to press, there were twenty-five of these, twenty-four in England, one in Wales. |
| PROTOTYPE ENVIRONMENTAL HOUSING | The Survivor House, Practical Alternatives, Victoria House, Bridge Street, Rhayader, Powys LD6 5AG (0597 810929). |
| | Low-Energy Self-Build House, Centre for Alternative Technology, Machynlleth, Powys, Wales SY20 9AZ (0654 2400). |
| RECYCLED PAPER SUPPLIES | A list of wholesale suppliers can be obtained on application to Friends of the Earth Trust Ltd., 26–28 Underwood Street, London N1 7QJ. Retail supplies can be obtained from: Traidcraft plc, Kingsway, Gateshead, Tyne and Wear NE11 0NE. Catalogue free on demand; Conservation Papers, 228 London Road, Reading, Berks RG6 1AH (0734 668611); British Paper Company, Frogmore Mill, Hemel Hempstead, Herts HP3 9RY (0442 231234); Paperback Ltd., 8–16 Coronet Street, London N1 6HD (01-729 1382). |
| RENEWABLE ENERGY | Details available from: Centre for Alternative Technology, Machynlleth, Powys, Wales SY20 9AZ, and: Renewable Energy Enquiries Bureau, Energy Technology Support Unit, Building 156, Harwell Laboratory, Oxon. OX11 0RA. Advice and information regarding grants from the EEC from: Commission of the European Communities, Director-General for Energy, Energy Demonstration Projects, rue de la Loi 200, B-1049 Brussels. |

| | |
|---|---|
| RUBBER AND PLASTICS (Research) | Materials Engineering Research Laboratory Ltd., Tamworth Road, Hertford SG13 7DG. |
| SICK BUILDING SYNDROME | Specialists are: Building Use Studies Ltd., 14–16 Stephenson Way, London NW1 2HD (01-387 3332). |
| SUSTAINABLE TIMBER SUPPLIES | Teak available from: James Latham (Northern) Ltd., Longlands, Ossett, West Yorkshire WF5 9JE. |
| TEXTILES RECYCLING | Expensive clothes can be sent to Barnardo's 'Textile Bank' at branches of Stepney Street, the first of which opened in May 1989 at 36 Westgate Street, Bath, Somerset. The clothes are remodelled by designers. To donate good quality clothing, cloth or trimmings telephone 0272 237270. |
| WASTE-HEAT RECOVERY | Details and 'Heat Recovery from High Temperature Waste Gas Streams' (Energy Technology Series, No. 6) available from: Enquiries Bureau, Energy Technology Support Unit, Building 156, Harwell Laboratory, Oxfordshire OX11 0RA. Technical information available from: Process Plant Association, 197 Knightsbridge, London SW7. |
| WATCHING WASTE IN THE COMMUNITY | Campaign run by National Council for Voluntary Organisations, 26 Bedford Square, London WC1B 3HU. |
| WOOD, SUSTAINABLE USAGE | Hooke Park College set up by Parnham Trust, Beaminster, Dorset DT8 3NA (0308 862204). |